The Incredible Media Quiz Book

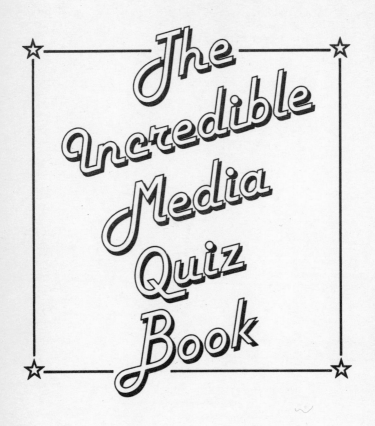

The Incredible Media Quiz Book

Angela Cockerill

First published in 1985 by
Octopus Books Limited
59 Grosvenor Street
London W1

© 1985 Hennerwood Publications
Limited

ISBN 0 86273 147 X

Printed and bound in Great Britain by
Collins Glasgow

Contents

Acknowledgements

The illustrations on pages 46-7 are reproduced by kind permission of the following organizations
1 Viacom Inc.
2, 3, 8 Warner Bros Inc (1984)
4, 6 © (1985) Hanna Barbera Productions, Inc.
5 Cosgrove Hall Productions Ltd.
7 (1985) United Artists Corporation ARR
9, 10 (1985) MGM/UA Entertainment Company ARR

Illustrations by
Mike Miller
Neil Sayer

Introduction

Well heartfaces, here it is at last. An entire quiz book totally devoted to the world of entertainment. Within the pages of this award-winning volume are a wealth of brain-taxing questions on films, pop, books, TV and radio, in fact enough questions on enough subjects to keep your brain busy for several eons.

TV is my favourite medium and I've been a fan ever since we got our first black-and-white set in Liverpool in 1953. I decided that watching TV was much more fun than watching radio and was hooked from the start. It was pretty grim in those days. (Cue violins.) There was only one channel called BBC Television! and programmes didn't actually start until 5 o'clock at night.

Nowadays of course people are bouncing colour TV pictures all over the place by those little wonders of science – satellites. I still find it amazing that a little box of tricks floating 22,000 miles above the Earth can zap live, moving pictures around the globe at the speed of light. Most things amaze me however, and I'm still baffled by radio!

As you may know, there is no end to the ingenuity of man, and it won't be long, if we don't blow ourselves up, 'til we have holographic films that spray 3-dimensional images into the middle of our laps. We'll be able to get up from our seats and walk around the actors for a better view of the scene.

Being an old pirate radio DJ, I was pleased to see a large part of the book devoted to pop questions, because I'm rather good at those! If you have any difficulty with the pop stuff, give my secretary a call and she'll arrange lunch and we'll iron the whole thing out.

Well, as Socrates once said, the future is before us. But before we leap into the void, take a little time dear reader to test your vast knowledge of the media in this, *The Incredible Media Quiz Book*. See if you can name the drummer in the Police or figure out what Farrah Fawcett Majors, Kate Jackson and Jaclyn Smith have in common, or name the two families in *Soap*.

I'm sure that this book will sharpen your mind, broaden your horizons and shiver your timbers. I'm also sure you'll have hours of pleasure figuring out the answers to questions like, 'Which stunningly talented, good looking, intelligent, sexy TV personality wrote the foreword to this book?'

Good guessing darling readers and remember . . . It's all written in the best POSSIBLE taste!!!

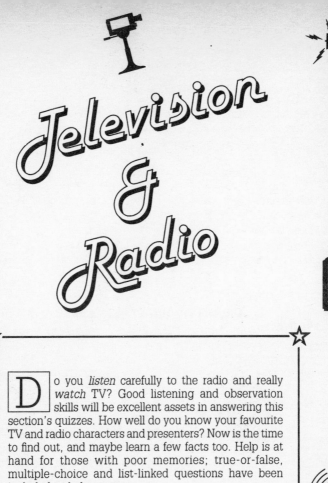

Television & Radio

D o you *listen* carefully to the radio and really *watch* TV? Good listening and observation skills will be excellent assets in answering this section's quizzes. How well do you know your favourite TV and radio characters and presenters? Now is the time to find out, and maybe learn a few facts too. Help is at hand for those with poor memories; true-or-false, multiple-choice and list-linked questions have been included to help you out.

There is something for all the family here, young and old. Who is the soap opera wizard in your family? Are you 'Top of the Form' with the police or comedy series? You will be challenged by the anagrams, and taken down memory lane by the nostalgia questions. Let's move on with the show and find your TV and radio mastermind.

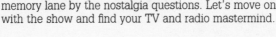

FAMILIES

In which television series would you learn of the exploits of the following families?

1 The Ewings
2 The Clampetts
3 The Sugdens
4 The Drummonds
5 The Grants
6 The Barlows
7 The Carringtons
8 The Cartwrights
9 The Ingles
10 The Hunters
11 The Tates
12 The Lamonts
13 The Dukes
14 The Pinners
15 The Laceys

SCORE 15 POINTS

WHO OR WHAT WAS IT?

Can you decide from the answers listed, the correct answers to the following?

1 With the exception of a brief stint by Nan Wilson in the late fifties, who is usually regarded as Britain's first woman newsreader. Was it: Jan Leeming, Selina Scott, Angela Rippon, Fern Britton?

2 After appearing in scores of films, Ellen Corby rose to fame with her role as Grandma in which series? Was it: *The Beverly Hillbillies, Falcon Crest, The Addams Family, The Waltons*?

3 Which popular comedian plays a Chinese character who calls everyone a 'stupid iriot'. Is it: Les Dawson, Lenny Henry, Benny Hill, Ernie Wise?

4 Which British general knowledge quiz is based on the American quiz *College Bowl*. Is it: *Mastermind, University Challenge, Top Of The Form, Blockbusters*?

5 Is the BBC's International Sheepdog Championship known as *Old Shep, The Shepherd, One Man And His Dog, Round 'Em Up*?

6 Which pop singer/film star narrated the stories of *Thomas The Tank Engine*? Was it: Ringo Starr, Davy Jones, David Bowie, Adam Ant?

SOLUTIONS ON PAGE 63

7 Airwolf was: a spaceship in a puppet series, an advanced combat helicopter, the leader of an SAS troop, an animal from outer space.

8 Eddie Shoestring was a young radio investigator played by: Gareth Hunt, Peter Egan, Trevor Eve, Malcolm Sinclair.

9 Who was the rugby league commentator who became popular in the television programme *It's A Knockout*? Was it: Eddie Waring, Dan Maskell, Ray French, Alex Murphy?

10 Which popular television actor, as juvenile played the title role in the original television version of *Just William*. Was it: Christopher Timothy, Jeffrey Holland, Richard Briers, Dennis Waterman?

SCORE 10 POINTS

ALL MIXED UP

Unscramble the letters and you will name some popular police and detective series.

1 HELL BIT   **2** GRIM TEA

SOLUTIONS ON PAGE 63

3	YES HE WET EN	**7**	RHOARY
4	CHAPS CLEAR BIN	**8**	TALES OF SHE PRISON
5	STARCHY DAN THUSK	**9**	THE GAVERNES
6	GUM MAN	**10**	BOOLCUM

SCORE 10 POINTS

PROGRAMME CHARACTERS

In which television series would you find the following characters?

1	Dusty Bin	**11**	Hannibal
2	The Fonz	**12**	Norman Stanley Fletcher
3	The Riddler	**13**	Hot Lips
4	Purdey	**14**	Regan
5	Gran Beales	**15**	Gunner Beaumont
6	Manuel	**16**	Dr Judith Vincent
7	Miss Jones	**17**	Yvonne Stuart-Hargreaves
8	Ida Willis	**18**	Zelda
9	A Time Lord	**19**	Spock
10	Dougal	**20**	Lucas Adams

SCORE 20 POINTS

SOLUTIONS ON PAGE 63

WHO AM I DESCRIBING?

1 She has been married to the actor Timothy West for more than twenty years and she partnered John Cleese, playing his wife Sybil in *Fawlty Towers*. Is she: Wendy Craig, Penelope Keith, Prunella Scales, Felicity Kendal?

2 Which British playwright and novelist wrote the first episode of *Upstairs, Downstairs* and serialised Jane Austen's *Pride And Prejudice* for television? Is it: Catherine Cookson, Virginia Wood, Paula Wilcox, Fay Weldon?

3 Which rotund American actor might you associate with the Domecq sherry commercials? Is it: Telly Savalas, Phil Silvers, Orson Welles, W C Fields?

4 Who was a Labour Member of Parliament for thirteen years before he went on to present London Weekend Television's current affairs programme *Weekend World*? Is it: Brian Walden, Peter Jay, Leonard Parkin, Frank Bough?

5 Which British actress was discovered in *Armchair Theatre* in 1959 and is known for her roles in the television series *Prince Regent, We'll Meet Again* and *Second Chance*? Is it: Susan Hampshire, Susannah York, Joanna Lumley, Yootha Joyce?

6 He began his career as a newscaster with ITN in 1955, before joining the BBC. He interviewed John F Kennedy in Britain in 1961. He has been with the programmes *Midweek* and *Tonight*. Is he: Sir Robin Day, Ludovic Kennedy, Richard Dimbleby, Julian Pettifer?

7 Who is the British light-entertainment comedian who is often seen as a pianist/composer/singer? He has also been associated with Andrew Lloyd-Webber in the production of a musical. Is it: Willie Rushton, Tony Selby, Melvyn Hayes, Richard Stilgoe?

8 Which toothy lady do you associate with the programmes *That's Life* and *The Big Time*? Is it: Frances de la Tour, Esther Rantzen, Angela Rippon, Sally Thomsett?

SOLUTIONS ON PAGE 64

9 Which successful and popular American television actress had three flops in the films *Somebody Killed Her Husband, Saturn 3* and *Sunburn*? Is it: Farrah Fawcett-Majors, Elaine Stritch, Goldie Hawn, Ali McGraw?

10 Who is the zany British comedian and former boxer who first came to public attention in *Who Do You Do*? Is it: Freddie Starr, Lenny Henry, Sidney James, Windsor Davies?

11 This British actor and writer was formerly an art teacher who became popular in the television series *Z Cars*. He has also written plays which include *Kisses At Fifty* and *Roll On Four O'Clock*. Who is he? Is it: Bernard Bresslaw, Colin Welland, Harry H Corbett, Derek Fowlds?

12 Who is the young Scottish entertainer who had a hit at the age of ten on *Opportunity Knocks* and later went on to have her own shows? Is it: Bonnie Langford, Lena Zavaroni, Joanne Ridley, Isla St Clair?

13 Who is the elegant Welsh actress who starred in *How Green Was My Valley, I Claudius* and *Churchill: The Wilderness Years*? Is it: Nerys Hughes, Angharad Rees, Megs Jenkins, Siân Phillips?

14 Which British actor, born 1920 began his career as a stage revue star in the fifties and went on to television, playing the roles of Bertie Wooster and Lord Peter Wimsey? Is it: Ian Carmichael, Harry Worth, George Cole, Peter Sallis?

15 Which television personality do you associate with woolly sweaters and a rocking chair? Is it: Bob Holness, Val Doonican, Terry Wogan, Michael Aspel?

SCORE 15 POINTS

FILL IN THE SPACE
Can you complete these sentences?

1 *Diff'rent Strokes* is a comedy series which involves three children, Kimberley, Arnold and _____.

SOLUTIONS ON PAGE 64

2 Lou Ferrigno was the American muscle man who played a lead in _____ _____ _____.

3 _____ and _____ were two puppet pigs, popular in early fifties and sixties programmes.

4 Morticia and Gomez are the parents of _____ and _____ in *The Addams Family*.

5 *Sanford And Son* was the American title for the British comedy programme _____ And _____.

6 _____ _____ became a television superstar when he played Eliot Ness in *The Untouchables*.

7 *Lou Grant* is set in the newsroom of a daily newspaper in _____ _____.

8 IBA's teletext service is called _____.

9 Herve Villechaize is the American dwarf actor featured in _____ _____.

SOLUTIONS ON PAGE 64

10 Ted Cassidy's height of 6'9" made him ideal for the role of _____ in *The Addams Family*.

SCORE 10 POINTS

CHILDREN ONLY

All of these questions relate to children's programmes. One point to children for each correct answer, two points for adults.

1 What is the name of the children's news quiz presented by Tommy Boyd?

2 Which programme has a quiz using a gigantic snakes and ladders board?

3 Which Cockney comedian presented *Runaround*?

4 Boxer, Wurzel and Hulk are all characters from which television series?

5 Who is the mascot of the *Children's ITV Club*?

6 What is the name of the rabbit in *The Magic Roundabout*?

7 Who is the Inspector who is helped to solve crimes by his niece Penny and his dog called Brain?

8 In which cartoon series do you meet Baron Greenback and Penfold?

9 Bobby Bins the dustman, Dr David Dimple and Dora the bus driver are all characters from which series?

10 Which famous bear lived in Jellystone National Park?

11 What is the name of the frog in *The Muppet Show*?

12 Which schoolboy from *Grange Hill* went on to have his own television series?

13 What are the christian names of The Krankies?

SOLUTIONS ON PAGE 64

14 What is Popeye's favourite food?

15 Kate Kestrel is a popular character from which television series?

16 In which city is *The Kids Of Degrassi Street* set?

17 Who succeeded his father in presenting television's *Sooty* shows?

18 Robin Williams played a confused alien in which comedy series?

19 Dick Dastardly and his pal Muttley are the villains of which cartoon series?

20 Mr Fisher and Mr Wheeler are gnomes from which television series?

SCORE 20 POINTS

SOLUTIONS ON PAGE 64

IN COMMON

In each question the programmes or personalities all have one obvious thing in common. Can you name it?

1 *Solo, Leaving* and *Butterflies* are all comedy series, they also have something else in common. What is it?

2 *Crossroads* is a regular soap opera, while *Last Of The Summer Wine* is a comedy. What do they have in common?

3 What do the actresses Katharine Blake, Googie Withers and Sarah Lawson have in common?

4 *The Boys From The Blackstuff* and *Scully* were both set in Liverpool. They also had something else in common. What is it?

5 *Surprise, Surprise* and *On Safari* have one thing in common, what is it?

6 Julia Somerville and Jan Leeming have one thing in common. Do you know what it is?

7 *The Irish RM* and *To The Manor Born* are both comedies, and also have another thing in common. What is it?

8 Tommy Trinder, Bruce Forsyth, Norman Vaughan and Jim Dale are all funny men. What other thing do they have in common?

9 What do the actors John Thaw and Jill Gascoine have in common?

10 What do the series *Sam's Luck, Sons And Daughters* and *A Country Practice* have in common?

11 What do Tom Baker, Jon Pertwee and Peter Davison have in common?

12 What do the silent comedy films *Futtock's End, The Picnic* and *By The Sea* have in common?

13 What do Farrah Fawcett-Majors, Kate Jackson and Jaclyn Smith have in common?

SOLUTIONS ON PAGE 64

14 What do Katherine Helmond, Donnelly Rhodes and Cathryn Damon have in common?

15 What do the programmes *Whiz Kids* and *Data Run* have in common?

SCORE 15 POINTS

CAN YOU IDENTIFY THE ACTOR?

Can you name the actor who appeared in both of the programmes listed?

1 *Bless Me, Father*, *Potter* and *A J Wentworth BA*

2 *The Lovers* and *Porridge*

3 *Gunsmoke* and *McCloud*

4 *Battlestar Galactica* and *Bonanza*

5 *The Professionals* and *Upstairs, Downstairs*

6 *Butterflies* and *Only Fools And Horses*

7 *The Zoo Gang* and *Young At Heart*

8 *The Detectives* and *Batman*

9 *Danger Man* and *The Prisoner*

10 *Doctor In Charge* and *Dick Turpin*

11 *Tenko* and *Sorrell And Son*

12 *For The Love Of Ada* and *The Nearly Man*

SOLUTIONS ON PAGE 65

13 *Romany Jones* and *Yus My Dear*
14 *It Takes A Thief* and *Colditz*
15 *The Rag Trade* and *On The Buses*
16 *Man About The House* and *Miss Jones And Son*
17 *The Fugitive* and *Harry O*
18 *Justice* and *Raffles*
19 *The Plane Makers* and *The Power Game*
20 *The Protectors* and *The Man From U.N.C.L.E.*

SCORE 20 POINTS

OCCUPATIONS

Can you link the appropriate occupation with the correct television character?

1 Bet Lynch
2 George Jackson
3 Timothy Lumsden
4 Stacy
5 Ted Bovis
6 Maggie Forbes
7 Jim Bergerac
8 Brabinger
9 Matt Skilbeck
10 Doris Luke
11 Mrs Slocombe
12 Latka
13 Major Sinclair Yeates
14 Michael Ranson
15 Tracy Willoughby

Nurse
Resident Magistrate
Detective Inspector
Barmaid
Butler
Shop Assistant
Surgeon
Fireman
Librarian
Comedian
Cleaner
Farmer
Detective
Motor Mechanic
Policewoman

SCORE 15 POINTS

TELEVISION QUIZZES

Can you name the questionmasters of the following television quizzes?

1 *Mr And Mrs*
2 *Mastermind*
3 *A Question Of Sport*
4 *Ask The Family*
5 *University Challenge*
6 *Odd One Out*
7 *What's My Line?*
8 *Double Your Money*
9 *Finders, Keepers*
10 *Family Fortunes*

SCORE 10 POINTS

SOLUTIONS ON PAGE 65

CAN YOU IDENTIFY THE ACTOR 2?

Can you name the actor who appeared in both of the programmes listed?

1 *Two's Company* and *Never The Twain*
2 *To The Manor Born* and *The Good Life*
3 *Only When I Laugh* and *When The Boat Comes In*
4 *Last Of The Summer Wine* and *The Kit Curran Radio Show*
5 *Minder* and *The Bounder*

6 *Tripper's Day* and *Rising Damp*
7 *Maggie And Her* and *Fresh Fields*
8 *That's My Boy* and *Are You Being Served?*
9 *Duty Free* and *Leaving*
10 *Rings On Their Fingers* and *Foxy Lady*

SCORE 10 POINTS

SPOT THE MISTAKE

In each of the following sentences which concern television comedy series there is a deliberate mistake. Can you spot the mistake?

1 Ria is tempted to stray from her husband by the debonair Thomas in the series *Butterflies*.

SOLUTIONS ON PAGE 66

2 Vince Warrender had left Penny at the altar on their wedding day and now they are 'just good friends'.

3 Neil Young sings the theme tune of the comedy series *Father's Day*.

4 Susan Hampshire and Anthony Booth played Martha and Daniel Ford, the parting couple in *Leaving*.

5 Bill Owen is popular as Foggy in *Last Of The Summer Wine*.

6 Jerry and Margo Leadbeatter are the more wealthy neighbours of the Goodwins in the hit comedy *The Good Life*.

7 Stile Prison is the home of Fletcher and Godber in *Porridge*.

8 Rodney, Dan and Great Uncle are the central characters in *Only Fools And Horses*.

9 John Alderton played the blustering teacher who attempted to teach English to foreign language students in *Mind Your Language*.

10 John Inman and Rula Lenska starred in a situation comedy concerning a female boss with a male secretary entitled *Take A Letter, Mr Smith*.

11 Rodney Bewes played the whining Terry in the comedy series set in the north east, called *The Likely Lads*.

12 Michael Bates is one of the actors in the popular comedy *It Ain't Half Hot Mum*, which is set in Korea.

13 Wilfred Brambell and Harry H Corbett played uncle and nephew in a long-running comedy series.

14 *Dad's Army* was a spin-off from the earlier series *The Army Game*.

15 Trevor and Vera Brown are the drop-in, animal-mad neighbours of the Crabtree's in *No Place Like Home*.

SOLUTIONS ON PAGE 66

16 *Never Mind The Quality, Feel The Width* was a series concerning a joinery business in London's East End, which starred Manny Cohen and Patrick Kelly.

17 Two girls sharing their flat with one man was the subject of the comedy *Robin's Nest*, which starred Sally Thomsett and Paula Wilcox.

18 Donny Osmond turned into a teenage idol after his starring role in the American comedy series, *The Partridge Family*.

19 Martin Jarvis is adept at playing bashful curates such as his roles in *All Gas And Gaiters*, *Oh Brother* and *Oh Father*.

20 Nyree Dawn Porter and Paul Daneman starred in the comedy series *Never The Twain*.

SCORE 20 POINTS

SOLUTIONS ON PAGE 67

HOW WELL DO YOU KNOW YOUR SOAPS?
Can you fill in the following blanks?

1 Amos Brearley and _____ _____ are the landlords of The _____ in *Emmerdale Farm*.

2 Angela Channing, the matriarch of Falcon Crest has two daughters _____ and _____.

3 Rita Fairclough, a one time nightclub singer, owns The _____ a small newsagents in *Coronation Street*.

4 Fallon Carrington decided her life was boring and empty, so her father gave her a hotel to manage which she named _____ _____.

5 Clive Hornby and Helen Weir, a married couple in real life, play _____ and _____ _____ in *Emmerdale Farm*.

6 Ken Barlow gave up his job at the community centre and became the editor of the local newspaper The _____ _____.

7 The comedy programme *Soap* parodies all soap operas and centres on the lives of two wildly eccentric families the _____ and the _____.

8 _____ _____ was the aristocratic sister of Clayton Farlow.

9 _____ _____ is the poacher-turned-gamekeeper in *Emmerdale Farm*.

10 _____ is the adopted son of Pam and Bobby Ewing.

11 The Rev Donald _____ the vicar of _____ attempts to bring his village flock together in harmony.

12 _____ _____ was a spin-off series from *Dallas* which featured _____ the black sheep of the Ewing family.

13 Mia Farrow and Ryan O'Neal were stars in the sixties soap opera _____ _____.

SOLUTIONS ON PAGE 67

14 _____ _____ and _____ are the elder children in the Grant household in Brookside Close.

15 The _____ was the first real soap opera in Britain. It starred Nancy Roberts as a testy old matriarch.

16 The Scottish soap opera *Take The High Road* is set around the fictitious highland community of _____.

17 _____, which was first transmitted in 1964, was originally known as *Midland Road*.

18 The Tilsley's live at number _____ Coronation Street.

19 The early sixties soap opera _____ was set in the offices of a woman's magazine.

20 _____ _____ was based on a book by Robert Wilder.

SCORE 20 POINTS

SOLUTIONS ON PAGE 68

THE COMEDIANS

Which famous comics do you associate with the following catch-phrases?

1 'Hello playmates...'
2 'Just like that...'
3 'I wanna tell you a story...'
4 'How tickled I am'
5 'Hello my darlings'
6 'She knows you know'
7 'Shut that door'
8 'It's goodnight from me and it's goodnight from him'
9 'Nice to see ya, to see ya, nice'
10 'Hmm Betty'
11 'You dirty old man'
12 'I only arsked ...'
13 'Yer actual ...'
14 'Bernie, the bolt'
15 'Oooh, you are awful – but I like you!'

SCORE 15 POINTS

POLICE

Can you pair the correct member of the police force with the television programme in which he or she appears?

1 Haskins	*Top Cat*
2 Detective Chief Inspector Bill Russell	*Kojak*
3 Detective Inspector Galloway	*Juliet Bravo*
4 Officer Dibble	*T. J. Hooker*
5 Inspector Barlow	*The Dukes Of Hazzard*
6 Inspector Kate Longton	*Hill Street Blues*
7 Romano	*The Bill*
8 Sheriff Rosco Coltrane	*The Gentle Touch*
9 Stavros	*Z Cars*
10 Captain Furillo	*The Sweeney*

SCORE 10 POINTS

TELEVISION CLASSICS

1 Can you name the actresses who played *The Avengers'* girls:
   a Cathy Gale
   b Emma Peel
   c Tara King
   d Purdy

SOLUTIONS ON PAGE 68

2 Which puppet did Annette Mills present on television in the fifties?

3 Who played the two wealthy adventurers who fought crime and corruption worldwide in the series *The Persuaders*?

4 Patrick McGoohan is well remembered for his portrayal of *Danger Man*. What was his name in the series?

5 Napoleon Solo and Illya Kuryakin were agents in which spy series?

6 Who rose to fame with his portrayal of Inspector Watt in *Z Cars*?

7 Patrick Mower and George Sewell were stars of which series which involved Scotland Yard security cases?

8 In a popular panel show of the sixties, guests were asked to comment on pop records, knowing that the pop artists were listening to their remarks. What was this programme called?

SOLUTIONS ON PAGE 69

9 George Simenon's books of a pipe-smoking Parisian sleuth were adapted for television. What was the name of this character?

10 Which metal monsters planned to 'exterminate' their enemies in *Dr Who*?

11 For which television role is the actress Dandy Nichols best known?

12 Whose orchestra was associated with the BBC's original ballroom dancing programme, *Television Dancing Club*?

13 Russell Hunter played opposite Edward Woodward in *Callan*. Can you remember the role he played?

14 Who played the starring role as the martial arts expert in *Kung Fu*?

15 Leonard Nimoy is forever associated with which cult television series? Which role did he play?

16 Whose name became synonymous with the role of Dr Kildare?

17 This talent-scout show ran from 1956-77 and introduced many stars to our screens for the first time. What was the name of this programme?

18 Can you name the popular western series of the sixties whose stories centred on the judge and where the ranch foreman was called Trampas?

19 For which television role did the actor Burt Ward become famous?

20 *Take Your Pick* began in 1955 and ran for nearly twenty years. Who was the questionmaster?

SCORE 20 POINTS

SOLUTIONS ON PAGE 69

TITLE ROLES

Which actors do you associate with the following title roles? If you answer without referring to the list of actors over the page score two points. If you refer to the list score one point. There are also a couple of red herrings in the list.

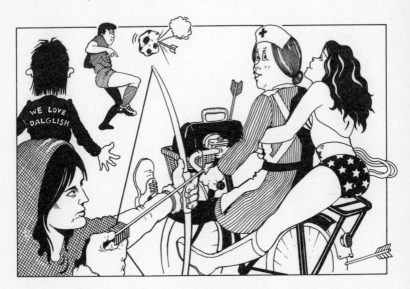

1 *Nanny*

2 *The District Nurse*

3 *Bergerac*

4 *Wonderwoman*

5 *The Duchess Of Duke Street*

6 *Mitch*

7 *Robin Of Sherwood*

8 *Scully*

9 *Sharon And Elsie*

10 *Shine On Harvey Moon*

11 *Alice*

12 *Hardcastle And McCormick*

13 *Jemima Shore Investigates*

14 *Quincy*

15 *Cagney And Lacey*

16 *The Black Adder*

17 *The Magnificent Evans*

18 *Rhoda*

19 *Reggie*

20 *Robin's Nest*

SOLUTIONS ON PAGE 69

Barry Evans	Linda Lavin
Lindsay Wagner	Valerie Harper
Richard O'Sullivan	Brian Keith and
Joanna Lumley and	Daniel Hugh-Kelly
David McCallum	Wendy Craig
Gemma Jones	John Thaw
Michael Praed	Ronnie Barker
Rowan Atkinson	Jack Klugman
Nerys Hughes	Patricia Hodge
Kenneth Cranham	Sharon Gless and Tyne Daly
Richard Mulligan	John Nettles
Andrew Scofield	Lynda Carter
Janette Beverly and Brigit Forsyth	Francoise Pascal

SCORE 20 POINTS (40 points without looking at the list)

TWENTY QUESTIONS

All of the twenty questions concern radio personalities. If you can answer each question without referring to the list of personalities score two points. Only one point if you look at the list.

1 Who is the distinguished broadcaster who devised *Hurrah For Hollywood* and was awarded the OBE in 1975 and the Variety Club Radio Personality of the Year Award in 1979?

2 David Jacobs lost his disc jockey image when he began presenting *Any Questions*. Who did he succeed in this role?

3 Which radio presenter has his own Late Show and made his name on television as a compere of *It's A Knock Out*?

4 Which broadcaster, who wrote the book *Eye Witness Falklands*, was awarded the MBE for his coverage of the Falklands War in 1982?

5 Who was the frontman for the comedy topical news show called *The News Huddlines*?

6 Which Cleveland M.P. joined Radio 1 from Radio Tees for the weekend early morning show?

SOLUTIONS ON PAGE 70

7 Which Liverpool son of a tug-boat captain began his broadcasting career on the pirate station Radio London in the early sixties?

8 Who was the comedian who created the garrulous funk disc jockey Delbert Wilkins, Eldreda the tea lady and the newsreader Trevor McDoughnut and tried them out on his radio audience?

9 Who was the Radio 1 disc jockey who interviewed John Lennon two days before his assassination?

10 Who was the BBC's Cricket Correspondent from 1963-72 who was named Radio's Male Personality of the Year in 1983?

11 Which comedy actress played Eth in the popular series *Take It From Here*?

12 Who am I describing? He was Foreign Correspondent for the BBC for 27 years, has written several books including *African Turmoil* and *German Notebook* together with a number of novels under the pseudonym William Fennerton.

SOLUTIONS ON PAGE 70

13 Which popular disc jockey began life as John Robert Parker Revenscroft?

14 Who was the Irish singer and broadcaster who was awarded the Variety Club's Personality of the Year Award in 1983?

15 Which cheerful personality do you associate with the long-running nationwide charity swap shop programme, *Sunday Soapbox*?

16 Paul Burnett, Tony Prince and Noel Edmonds were all involved with which foreign radio station?

17 By what name is the actor Norman Painting, who according to *The Guinness Book Of Records* is the longest running 'Archer', more commonly known?

18 Who was the BBC's Cricket Correspondent from 1974-80 and author of *Bedside Cricket* and *The Complete Who's Who Of Test Cricketers*?

19 Which of television's *Game For A Laugh* presenters had his own radio programme *Nightcap*?

20 Who was with the pirate radio stations, Radio Caroline South and Radio London before working for the BBC in 1967?

Charlie Chester	Brian Johnston
Mark Page	Roy Plomley
June Whitfield	Gloria Hunniford
Luxembourg	Tony Blackburn
Freddy Grisewood	Robert Fox
John Peel	Phil Archer
Lenny Henry	Christopher Martin Jenkins
Ian McDougall	Andy Peebles
Kenny Everett	Stuart Hall
Jeremy Beadle	Roy Hudd

SCORE 20 POINTS (40 points without looking at the list)

SOLUTIONS ON PAGE 70

RADIO PRESENTERS

Can you link the following radio presenters with the list of programmes most associated with them? Score one point for each
correct answer.

1 Sue MacGregor
2 Derek Cooper
3 Andy Peebles
4 Barry Norman
5 Jimmy Savile
6 Alistair Cooke
7 Tim Gudgin and
 Paddy Feaney
8 Louise Botting
9 Nigel Rees
10 Jimmy Young

Money Box
My Top Ten
Woman's Hour
Quote ... Unquote
The Chip Shop
The Night Is Young
The Food Programme

Letter From America
_____ _____ *Old Record Club*
Top Of The Form

SCORE 10 POINTS

SOLUTIONS ON PAGE 70

BREAKFAST TEASER

Hidden below are personalities from BBC's *Breakfast Time* and ITV's *Good Morning Britain*. To make your task of finding the names of the personalities a little easier, we have given you some clues. The names of the personalities can run horizontally, vertically or diagonally. Some run backwards. All the names run in an uninterrupted straight line.

```
G U B O T N A R G L L E S S U R A D
A L P T C G H F K E M D N C B J E F
V Q Y D S E L I N A S C O T T Z C H
Z T R N E S I L L I W Y E C N I W I
B U S F N B I J H L F W E M Y B O R
C A W S L C G U M V G K X D C L N O
R V M X Y T H R I I P H L A K Z G R
Z Y A X N G S R J B K O B A J X P D
Y D D Q N R M K I N I E I R S Q Y Y
E N L G F E L A D S J W S V W G F L
H F I I A E E M A K T H L M N O T L
T O Z H U N T N V G B I D U I U P E
I P Z O L G T N I F X E A T I T H W
M J I N D O E H D I C K L N R V H E
S K E W S D N O F J E Y A J S Q D L
D P L Q W D R G R F M B E W H S E L
R P M L O E A P O Z D N O G P R B Y
A Q N M O S B A S B L C U T N O A N
H O P K D S I Q T B A O U E B B J Y
C U R Q J I N I L J B M W W D K C B
I R T S O H E S R K N O I M W X R Z
R V G C U Z J T N S K L I Y G E F A
R H D N F G D A T C S J X H V M Q U
D F E C W V R U I O K V K A N X T W
A Z B Y X F E N N L W L N Y O P S C
```

CLUES

1 Born in New Zealand, he wrote *The No-cook Cook Book*, *Fragile Paradise* and *Guide To Delicatessen Food*.
2 He won the Richard Dimbleby Award (BAFTA) for his outstanding contribution to factual television in 1977. He has also written a book entitled *Cue Frank*.

SOLUTIONS ON PAGE 70

3 This lady came into television because of her interest in animals. She is known as a weather lady.

4 You can shake out your early morning aches and pains with this lady.

5 Consumer headaches are no problem for this Scottish lady.

6 Tune in for your pop report with this man who was once Noel Edmond's chauffeur.

7 *Breakfast Time*'s own doctor.

8 She has a 'Pick of the Week' slot on *Good Morning Britain*.

9 This man has green fingers.

10 A regular *Good Morning Britain* presenter.

11 This former Arsenal and Scotland goalkeeper will keep you up to date with the sporting news.

12 This zany astrologer might brighten up your day.

13 Diana Moran's nickname.

14 The female half of *Breakfast Time*.

15 One of *TV AM*'s Famous Five.

SCORE 15 POINTS

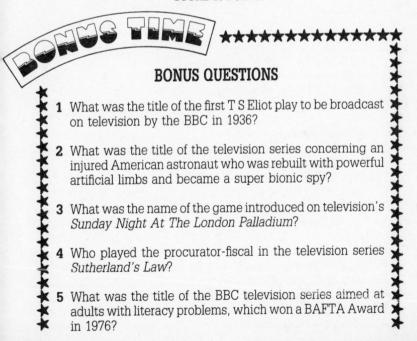

BONUS TIME

BONUS QUESTIONS

1 What was the title of the first T S Eliot play to be broadcast on television by the BBC in 1936?

2 What was the title of the television series concerning an injured American astronaut who was rebuilt with powerful artificial limbs and became a super bionic spy?

3 What was the name of the game introduced on television's *Sunday Night At The London Palladium*?

4 Who played the procurator-fiscal in the television series *Sutherland's Law*?

5 What was the title of the BBC television series aimed at adults with literacy problems, which won a BAFTA Award in 1976?

SOLUTIONS ON PAGE 71

6 Which actress played the spoilt daughter in the television drama series *Bouquet Of Barbed Wire*?

7 What is the title of Anglia television's wildlife film series which has run since the fifties?

8 Who created the character Van Der Valk, the Dutch police inspector in the popular seventies television series?

9 Who played the male title role in the highly acclaimed television series *Edward And Mrs Simpson*?

10 The songs 'Hi-Fidelity' (1982) and 'Starmaker' (1982) were featured in which television series?

11 With which popular television series would you connect the film *The Homecoming*?

12 Who is the British actor and quizmaster who was once a stooge for Arthur Haynes?

SOLUTIONS ON PAGE 71

13 Who was the British archaeologist who was popular in the fifties television panel game, *Animal, Vegetable And Mineral*?

14 Which piece of music introduced the seventies television series *Read All About It*?

15 Who was the child actress who made her comeback in the television play *Cathy Come Home*?

16 In the radio serial *The Archers*, what are the names of Phil and Jill Archer's children?

17 What is the name of Roger Cook's award-winning, investigative radio programme?

18 Mr What's-'is-name, Ali Oop, Claude and Cecil and Colonel Chinstrap were all popular characters from which radio series?

19 Name the actors who played the following radio characters in *The Goons*:
a Neddie Seagoon
b Eccles
c Bluebottle

20 Which of The Goons' songs entered the British pop charts in 1956 and again in 1973?

SCORE 2 POINTS FOR EACH CORRECT ANSWER

ADVERTISEMENTS

Name the products or services which have been advertised with the following slogans:

1 'WotalotIgot'
2 'It looks good, it tastes good, and by golly it does you good'
3 '. . . the margarine for men'
4 'Naughty, but nice'
5 'Sccchhh . . . you know who'

SOLUTIONS ON PAGE 71

6 'The Listening Bank'

7 'Soft, strong and very long'

8 'Can you tell . . . from butter'

9 'Go to work on an . . .'

10 'Fresh . . . gotta lotta bottle'

11 'Beanz Meanz . . .'

12 'Don't say vinegar say . . .'

13 'Wake up to what . . . is doing'

14 'Keep it with . . .'

15 'Coffee at its best'

SCORE 15 POINTS

ODD ONE OUT

One of the television characters in each of the following is an odd one out. Can you identify the character for one point and the programme in which the others appear for an additional point?

1 Shorofsky, Doris, Miss Jones, Bruno Martelli

2 Rose Millar, Blanche, Christina Campbell, Joss Holland

3 Mavis Hooper, Benny Hunter, Jill Chance, Miranda Pollard

4 Fred Quilly, Mr Grouse, Ted Bovis, Sylvia

5 Uncle Jester, Daisy, Enos, Boss Hogg

6 Margaret Frogerty, Mrs Polouvicka, Ned, Richard De Vere

7 Claire Scott, Zammo, Stewpot Stevens, Mr Browning

8 Suzanne, Hannibal, Murdock, Baracus

SOLUTIONS ON PAGE 71

9 Detective Sergeant Jake Barratt, Simon Forbes, Detective Sergeant Peter Phillips, Detective Inspector Mike Turnbull
10 Angela Channing, Maggie Channing, Lance, Chase Gioberti

SCORE 20 POINTS

COMPLETE THE LINE

For ten points, complete the following horizontal words from the clues given and reveal the name of a well-known television character.

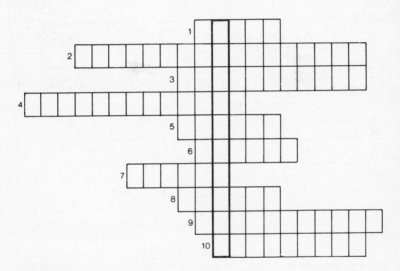

CLUES

1 Jon and Ponch are the stars of this television series.
2 Hughie Green hosted this talent show.
3 This Scottish presenter found fame on *The Generation Game*.
4 Polly James and Nerys Hughes were the original stars of this comedy series.
5 The name of the central family from *When The Boat Comes In*.
6 Bernard Hill's role in *Boys From The Blackstuff*.
7 The surname of the sports commentator who compered *It's A Knockout*.
8 The butler in *Upstairs, Downstairs*.

SOLUTIONS ON PAGE 72

9 Nigel Hawthorne, Paul Eddington and Derek Fowlds star in this popular comedy.

10 Surname of the woman who won £152,000 on the football pools, who was the subject of the documentary *Spend, Spend, Spend*.

SCORE 10 POINTS

WHERE DID I HEAR THAT?????????

Below are a list of common slogans and general sayings which have become popular on radio. Can you identify either the personality who makes the remark or the programme on which you would hear the comment?

1 'Hi there pop-pickers!'

2 'And now here is next week's news'

3 'Orft we jolly well go!'

4 'Are you sitting comfortably? Then I'll begin'

5 'How's about that then, guys and gals?'

6 'Oooo arr, me ol' pal, me ol' beauty!'

7 'And a very good morning to you!'

8 'Let's fight the flab'

9 'Woof-woof' (said Arnold)

10 'Ello darlin!'

SCORE 10 POINTS

SELECT ONE

How well do you know your radio programmes? Select what you believe to be the correct answer from the choices given.

1 Brian Redhead and John Timpson are associated with the news programme called:
a *The World At One*
b *Today*
c *The Six O'Clock News*
d *News Briefing*

2 The award winning medical journalist Geoff Watts presents a medical radio series entitled:
a Medicine Now
b Just What The Doctor Ordered
c Bedside Manner
d I Don't Feel Well ...

SOLUTIONS ON PAGE 72

3 Tony Blackburn's Radio 1 *Breakfast Show* opened on the 30 September in the year:

a 1965   **b** 1966   **c** 1967   **d** 1968

4 In the long running radio series *The Archers*, what is the title of the signature tune:

a Ambridge Village
b Eddie's Song
c Barwick Green
d The Archers And Friends

5 Bernard Falk is one of the presenters of a popular programme on travel, leisure and holiday information. It is called:

a Holidaytime
b Any Time Of The Year
c Breakaway
d We're All Going On A Summer Holiday

6 The initials CB represent:

a Community Banter
b Citizen's Band
c Citizen Breakers
d Collective Band

SOLUTIONS ON PAGE 73

7 What is the name of the reply programme to David Jacob's radio programme *Any Questions*:
 a Any Answers
 b Not Today, Thank You
 c No Questions, No Answers
 d Why? Why? Why?

8 Which country has the largest number of radio broadcasting stations:
 a India
 b Britain
 c America
 d Russia

9 Ford Prefect was a character in the radio series called:
 a *It's That Man Again*
 b *The Hitchhikers Guide To The Galaxy*
 c *Educating Archie*
 d *The Archers*

10 *Down Your Way* travels around the country talking to a wide variety of people in different occupations and with varied ways of life. Who presents this programme:
 a Robert Robinson
 b Brian Johnston
 c Sue MacGregor
 d Gloria Hunniford

SCORE 10 POINTS

FILL IN THE SPACES

Can you complete the following sentences about radio by filling in the blank spaces with the correct answers?

1 The four who originally made up the hilarious programme *The Goon Show* were Spike Milligan, Peter Sellers, Harry Secombe and _____ _____.

2 This comedian was popular on radio with his own thirty minute show called _____ *Half Hour*.

SOLUTIONS ON PAGE 73

3 ＿＿＿ ＿＿＿ ＿＿＿ is known as the 'hairy monster'.

4 The disc jockey ＿＿＿ ＿＿＿ is Keith Chegwin's sister.

5 News, views and information for people with a visual handicap can be heard on Radio 4's *In* ＿＿＿.

6 ＿＿＿ ＿＿＿ is the disc jockey who provided his listeners with the opportunity to share their romantic memories with others in his *Our Tune* slot on his programme.

7 ＿＿＿ ＿＿＿ became the first woman DJ on Radio 1 in 1970.

8 ＿＿＿ ＿＿＿ sets the questions and is the questionmaster of *Round Britain Quiz* and *Round Europe Quiz*.

9 Walter Gabriel's son in *The Archers* is called ＿＿＿.

10 Gloria Hunniford, Jimmy Young and Ray Moore are principally concerned with Radio ＿＿＿.

SCORE 10 POINTS

SOLUTIONS ON PAGE 73

CARTOON CHARACTERS
Can you identify the following characters?

1

2

3

4

5

SOLUTIONS ON PAGE 73

SOLUTIONS ON PAGE 73

NEWSREADERS

Choose the correct answers from those listed.

1 Who became the first newsreader on television in 1957, a job he/she held for more than a quarter of a century? Frank Bough, Richard Whitmore, Richard Baker, Frances Coverdale.

2 Which former BBC newsreader made his first radio broadcast in 1954 in a Children's Hour play and later went on to host children's shows and *Miss World*? Terry Wogan, Michael Aspel, Noel Edmonds, John Craven.

3 Doc Cox and Joanna Monro were at which newsdesk? *News At One, The Six O'Clock News, Not The Nine O'Clock News, That's Life, Newsdesk.*

4 Which former ITN reporter wrote the plays *Harry's Game* and *The Glory Boys* which were both dramatised for ITV? Leonard Parkin, Gerald Seymour, Anna Ford, Reginald Bosanquet.

5 Which television news presenter wrote a biography of the great batsman Viv Richards? Trevor McDonald, Tom Kilgour, Jeremy Paxman, Peter Sissons.

SOLUTIONS ON PAGE 73

6 Which former newsreader presented the television magazine programme for older viewers entitled *Years Ahead*? Robert Dougal, Robert Robinson, Gordon Clough, Richard Kershaw.

7 Which Radio 1 disc jockey joined the BBC in 1973 as a Radio 2 announcer and newsreader? Simon Bates, Paul Gambaccini, Janice Long, Tony Blackburn.

8 Which co-presenter of Radio 4's *Today* programme chaired the *Mastermind Of Gardening Finals* in 1981, '82 and '83? John Craven, Peter Hobday, John Timpson, Brian Widlake.

9 Who was the front man of the television news magazine *Tonight*, who married the lady on the other end of the line in *Two Way Family Favourites*? Cliff Michelmore, David Dimbleby, Nicholas Witchell, Sir Robin Day.

10 Who was an ITN newsreader before she teamed up with Frank Bough for *Breakfast Time*? Jan Leeming, Debbie Rix, Selina Scott, Fern Britton.

SCORE 10 POINTS

DISC JOCKEYS

Can you identify the disc jockeys from their brief biographies?

1 Born in Buxton in Derbyshire _____ _____ _____ began his broadcasting career on the pirate station, Radio Caroline (South).

2 'It's all done in the best possible taste ...' is a catchphrase of _____ _____.

3 _____ _____ began his career as a newsreader on Radio Luxembourg in 1968 and gained his big break when he stepped in for Kenny Everett who was ill.

4 _____ _____ is an American who went to Oxford University and now presents his own US chart show on Radio 1.

5 _____ _____ introduced the Miss World Contest in 1978 on the BBC.

SOLUTIONS ON PAGE 73

6 T.T.F.N. was _____ _____'s signing off catchphrase.

7 _____ _____ *In The Afternoon* is a regular daily Radio 1 show by a former Radio Luxembourg disc jockey.

8 _____ _____ has hosted television's *Miss TV Times, World Disco Dance Championships* and *Seaside Special* and is often nicknamed 'Diddy'.

9 _____ _____ was the young Canadian disc jockey who had the nickname 'Kid'.

10 Ollie, _____ _____'s wife, co-presents many radio programmes and has become a popular presenter on Radio Luxembourg.

SCORE 10 POINTS

CORONATION STREET

Coronation Street was first transmitted in December 1960 and continues twice-weekly after all this time. How well do you know 'the Street' and its characters?

1 Who played Elsie Tanner from the first episode in 1960 until November 1983?

2 Which actor played Johnny Webb, Eddie Yeats' dustman friend in 1980?

3 Who died from a heart attack in the Rover's snug on 13 May 1964?

4 Who did Harry Hewitt marry on 1 October 1961?

5 Who had second thoughts about marrying Lucille Hewitt and cancelled the wedding?

6 Which baby was born on 24 January 1977 while her father Ray, was at a dance?

7 What were the names of Ken Barlow's twins by his wife Valerie?

SOLUTIONS ON PAGE 74

8 How did Valerie Barlow die?

9 Who died while on a driving lesson with her husband in July 1980?

10 Elsie Tanner's daughter Linda married a Hungarian refugee. What was his name?

11 Who refused to marry Mike Baldwin after having his illegitimate child?

12 What type of business does Brian Tilsley practice?

13 Who was the local joiner and builder in the street, who also owned a newsagents?

14 Who lived at number thirteen Coronation Street?

15 Who was the licensee of The Rover's Return?

16 What is Mike Baldwin's favourite tipple?

17 Name the barmaid known for her extravagant gaudy taste in earrings?

18 Who was the old lady with the hairnet who liked her half of stout?

19 The actor Graham Haberfield died suddenly on 10 November 1975, which role did he play in the series?

20 Who did Eddie Yeats marry at All Saints Church, Weatherfield in October 1983?

SCORE 20 POINTS

IT'S A LAUGH

How well do you know your television comedies? Below are some questions on old favourites, together with some new series.

1 What is the relationship between Tom and Toby in *Don't Wait Up*?

SOLUTIONS ON PAGE 74

2 Who are Tom and Barbara's next door neighbours in *The Good Life*?

3 What was the title of the comedy which concerned a working class bigot with black neighbours, which starred Jack Smethurst and Nina Baden-Semper?

4 The Fourmiles were the next door neighbours of the Ropers in *George and Mildred*. What was the name of the Fourmiles' son?

5 Lorna Patterson played the title role in a television series (which was also a film) concerning a rich girl unused to army ways. What was the title of the television series?

6 What is the name of Fred Moffat's secretary in *The Gaffer*?

7 What are the christian names of *Cannon And Ball*?

8 Which endearing comedy actress played 'Mrs P' in *Maggie And Her*?

9 Which comedy series starred Jennifer Lonsdale, Christopher Blake and Mollie Sugden?

SOLUTIONS ON PAGE 74

10 The saga of two couples on a package holiday in Spain produced which comedy series?

11 Sir John Mills and Megs Jenkins were a retired couple in which sentimental comedy?

12 Frankie Howerd played a Roman slave in a BBC comedy adapted from the stage show *A Funny Thing Happened On The Way To The Forum*. What was the title of this series?

13 Tracey Ullman, Lenny Henry and which other comedian made up *Three Of A Kind*?

14 What was the name of the slow, kiss-curled private played by Bernard Bresslaw in *The Army Game*?

15 Daisy Troop and Kate Codd were the central characters in which comedy series of the eighties?

16 Who played the title role in *Father, Dear Father*?

17 Benson had his own comedy series, what was the name of the Governor in this series?

18 Who are television's funny *Dear Ladies*?

19 Jeffrey Fairbrother was the unsure, nervous archaeology professor in which comedy series?

20 What is Rhoda's surname?

SCORE 20 POINTS

HOW WELL DO YOU KNOW YOUR SOAPS 2?

1 Can you name the brewery that supplies The Rover's Return?

2 Who am I describing? In her late twenties, this beautiful lady is separated from her husband Roger and is progressing well in her career in accountancy.

3 Who was Ken Barlow's female assistant on the newspaper?

SOLUTIONS ON PAGE 74

4 Which of the Carrington clan lived in Billings, Montana for more than twenty years?

5 What is the name of Ray Krebbs' beautiful wife?

6 Who had a test-tube baby in *Crossroads*?

7 In which television soap opera does the lawyer Phillip Erikson appear?

8 What type of business did Terry, Barry, Celia and Michelle open in *Brookside*?

9 Who was credited with making *Dallas* a success by constantly knocking it on his radio show?

10 Den Watts is the gov'nor of which pub in *The EastEnders*?

11. What is unique about the actor Al Dixon's role in *Emmerdale Farm*?

12 Name Bill Webster's two teenage children?

13 Which famous film actress plays the vineyard heiress, Angela Channing in *Falcon Crest*?

14 What is the fictional location of *Crossroads*?

15 Who did Jeff marry after his divorce from Fallon?

16 Which role did Elvis Presley's ex-wife play in *Dallas*?

17 Who is the caretaker of the community centre in *Coronation Street*?

18 Who is the lady laird in *Take The High Road*?

19 Who is the star-gazing dustman in *Coronation Street*?

20 What is the name of JR's only son?

SCORE 20 POINTS

SOLUTIONS ON PAGE 74

FILL IN THE BLANKS

1 Bill _____ and _____ _____ are the resident team captains in *A Question Of Sport*.

2 David Frost hosted _____ _____ which began with one thousand contestants setting out to win the largest prize on British television.

3 The 'Gold Run' was a prize winning feature of _____.

4 Fred Dineage hosted the nostalgic _____ _____ and _____ _____ _____ kept the score.

5 Contestants in *Bullseye* are challenged to gamble their prizes for a star prize hiding behind bully if they can score _____ in _____ darts.

6 Hughie Green hosted the old favourite *Double Your Money*. _____ _____ was the cockney hostess who became a personality on the quiz.

7 _____ _____ is the longest running quiz show on British television.

8 _____ _____ took over from _____ _____ on *Family Fortunes*.

9 The distinguished broadcaster _____ _____ turned Quizmaster for the *Busman's Holiday* programme.

10 John Julius Norwich and John Carter were the resident captains of the holiday and travel quiz called _____ _____ _____ _____.

11 _____ _____ and _____ were the resident songsters on Lionel Blairs *Name That Tune*.

12 _____ _____ hosted the challenge quiz *Gambit*.

13 'Come on Down' are the words each audience member longs to hear on _____ _____ _____ _____.

SOLUTIONS ON PAGE 75

14 _____ _____ hosted the old favourite *Take Your Pick*.

15 'Trains And Boats And Planes' is the signature tune for _____ _____ _____ _____.

SCORE 15 POINTS

TWENTY QUESTIONS

1 What was the name of the gambler played by Ray Brooks in *Big Deal*?

2 Linda and Robert Cochran were one of the couples in the comedy series *Duty Free*. Can you name the other couple?

3 Who was the comedienne who played Hilary Myers, the TV researcher in *Hilary*?

4 Richard Briers, Penelope Wilton and Peter Egan played Martin, Ann and Paul in which popular comedy series?

5 Which programme was set in Stackton Tressel?

6 In which television programme would you hear the words, 'To boldly go where no man has gone before'?

7 What was the name of the police TV series which was inspired by the 1968 film *Coogan's Bluff*?

8 Who composed the title music for the comedy series *Me And My Girl*?

9 Name the street where Jim London lived in *Up The Elephant And Round The Castle*.

10 Craig Stirling and Sharron Macready were the superhumans in which television series?

11 Which actress played Captain Emily Ridley in the comedy series *Hallelujah*?

SOLUTIONS ON PAGE 75

12 Name the police station in *Juliet Bravo*.

13 What, or who was TV's Street Hawk?

14 Which television personality was known for his comment, 'And this is me . . .'?

15 'The Dolly Dealers' were a feature of which television game show?

SCORE 15 POINTS

TV PERSONALITIES
Are you able to identify the following television personalities?

1 She is the younger daughter of Baron and Lady Harmer-Nicholls. She is known particularly for her role as Audrey Potter in *Coronation Street* and played Wanda Pickles in *Up The Elephant And Round The Castle*.

2 He was born in Dublin in 1922 and began his career as a boxing commentator on radio in 1939. He was a former All-Ireland Amateur Junior Boxing Champion. His TV work includes *Crackerjack*, *World Of Sport* and *Time For Business*.

3 Born in 1910, she established herself in TV in 1979 and won the TV Personality of the Year Award. She has an entry in the *Guinness Book Of Records* for her work with animals. Her autobiography, and 17th book, was *Talking To The Animals*.

4 He was originally a teacher of maths and music in Bootle. He became a full-time entertainer in 1974 and after *Opportunity Knocks* he was given his own show. His 'hobbies' include golf, snooker and football.

5 Born in 1942 in Kent, this newscaster/interviewer had 15 years experience in radio, theatre and TV in Australia and New Zealand before spending six years with HTV. Gained the News-reader of the Year Award in 1981.

SOLUTIONS ON PAGE 75

6 This TV Journalist was born in Blackburn, Lancashire. He has been a chat-show host since 1971. He won an International Emmy for his programme *Hello Dali.*

7 This actor's first big break was in *Love For Lydia* which he followed with *All Creatures Great And Small.* He is married to the actress Sandra Dickinson.

8 This disc jockey turned TV presenter originally trained as a teacher. He pioneered a new phone-in show for children. His other work includes *Come Dancing, Taking The Strain* and *Top Gear.*

9 This reporter/presenter worked freelance for the BBC. Shows include *Tomorrow's World* and *Family Scientist. But What About The Children?* and *The Perfect Baby* are amongst her books.

10 This actress is well-known for her stage appearances and has also worked in radio, films and TV. Her TV work includes *The Lovers, Doctor At Large* and *Give Us A Clue.* She is married to a famous playwright.

11 *The Yo-Yo Man* is the autobiography of this actor, born in Surrey. He has spent time in the theatre and pantomime and he made his film debut in *Till Death Us Do Part.* His TV work includes *The Life Of Riley, The Gaffer* and *Coronation Street.*

12 This interviewer and TV Producer was an English and Sports teacher. She co-presented *Tea Break* with her husband in 1972. Other programmes include *After Noon* and *After Noon Plus.*

13 She went to Oxford and read English. She joined the BBC as a radio effects girl and later went into research. She is particularly identified with one show, which she has presented and produced since 1973.

14 This actor/comedian originally studied accountancy but went into the Royal Navy after his war service. He is seen on stage and in pantomime and has acted in many *Carry On* films. His TV series include *Son Of The Bride* and *Happy Ever After.*

SOLUTIONS ON PAGE 75

15 This London-born ventriloquist originally worked in the Stock Exchange. After ten years in show business he became an overnight success after appearing on *New Faces*.

SCORE 15 POINTS

TELEVISION FEATURES

Can you answer the following?:

1 If Eamonn Andrews walked up to you with a big red book under his arm, what would you expect him to say?

2 Penny Babcock's tongue twister is a feature of which programme?

3 According to Bruce Forsyth in *Play Your Cards Right*, what do points make?

4 The Golden Egg Awards are a feature of whose programme?

5 Who in the world of entertainment is known as 'the one with the short, fat, hairy legs'?

SOLUTIONS ON PAGE 76

6 'Kemo Sabe' was whose famous greeting in *The Lone Ranger*?

7 Which programme features 'The Bunco Booth'?

8 Who refers to his television wife as 'her indoors'?

9 Star prizes are won on completion of 'The Golden Run' in which programme?

10 In which programme did a son refer to his father as 'You dirty old man'?

11 In which programme was there an obstacle known as Biggin's Jungle Course?

12 Which actress came to prominence by saying, in the much loved Campari commercial: 'No, Luton Airport'?

13 Who is television's Captain Kremmen?

14 Statler and Waldorf are aged hecklers in which television programme?

15 Which television character constantly says 'Oh Betty!' to his wife when he gets flustered?

SCORE 15 POINTS

CROSSROADS

Crossroads Motel first opened its doors in 1964. How much do you know of the Crossroads world and its characters?

1 Which of Meg's husbands was an inveterate gambler and insured her life before setting out to kill her?

2 What was the name of Diane's postman husband?

3 Jill Chance's daughter lives with her father and his new wife in Germany. What is the name of Jill's only daughter?

SOLUTIONS ON PAGE 76

4 Stan Harvey's sister Sheila worked at the motel until her marriage to Roy Mollison. What was Sheila's job at the motel?

5 Name the actor who has played David Hunter, the suave motel director since the start of the Crossroads series.

6 Barbara Hunter is a director of the motel, but she also has another occupation. What is it?

7 Benny is the simple-minded lovable character from *Crossroads* who is always trying to help everyone. What is his surname?

8 Diane made a marriage of convenience with David Hunter's son. What was the son's name?

9 What is the relationship between J Henry Pollard and Miranda Pollard?

10 When Meg left the motel for good, where was she travelling to?

11 Which character is played by Rowena Wallace in *Sons And Daughters*?

12 Which role does Sandor Eles play in the series?

13 Kath Brownlow's husband Arthur died suddenly, how did this happen?

14 What was the name of the motel garage foreman who had suffered from racial harassment?

15 Who did Meg Richardson marry in 1975?

SCORE 15 POINTS

TELEVISION CHARACTERS

Are you able to identify the television programmes in which the following characters appear? For those who need a little help there is a list below, but with some red herrings!

1 Huggy Bear   **11** Bull Shannon

SOLUTIONS ON PAGE 76

2 B. A. Baracus
3 Stacy
4 Sir Humphrey Appleby
5 Joyce Davenport
6 Stringfellow Hawke
7 Nell Cresset
8 Aunt Clara
9 Coryell
10 Kate Moses

12 Mrs Van Meyer
13 Coach Ernie Pantusso
14 Steve Forbes
15 Morticia
16 Oz
17 Wojo
18 Brabinger
19 Diamante Lil
20 Paddy Reilly

T. J. Hooker
Hill Street Blues
Blue Peter
Me And My Girl
Shelley
The Yellow Rose
Widows
Cheers
Auf Wiedersehen, Pet
Starsky And Hutch
Inside Out
To The Manor Born
Bewitched

Crossroads
The A Team
Night Court
Barney Miller
Yes, Minister
The Gentle Touch
One By One
Brookside
Coronation Street
Airwolf
The High Chapparal
Emmerdale Farm
Tenko

SCORE 20 POINTS

SOLUTIONS ON PAGE 76

FAMILIES

1 *Dallas*
2 *The Beverley Hillbillies*
3 *Emmerdale Farm*
4 *Diff'rent Strokes*
5 *Brookside*
6 *Coronation Street*
7 *Dynasty*
8 *Bonanza*
9 *The Little House On The Prairie*
10 *Crossroads*
11 *Soap*
12 *Take The High Road*
13 *The Dukes Of Hazzard*
14 *Just Good Friends*
15 *Cagney And Lacey*

WHO OR WHAT WAS IT?

1 Angela Rippon
2 *The Waltons*
3 Benny Hill
4 *University Challenge*
5 *One Man And His Dog*
6 Ringo Starr
7 An advanced combat helicopter
8 Trevor Eve
9 Eddie Waring
10 Dennis Waterman

ALL MIXED UP

1 *The Bill*
2 *Maigret*
3 *The Sweeney*
4 *Special Branch*
5 *Starsky And Hutch*
6 *Magnum*
7 *Harry O*
8 *The Professionals*
9 *The Avengers*
10 *Columbo*

PROGRAMME CHARACTERS

1 *3-2-1*
2 *Happy Days*
3 *Batman*
4 *The New Avengers*
5 *The East Enders*
6 *Fawlty Towers*
7 *Rising Damp*
8 *That's My Boy*
9 *Dr Who*
10 *The Magic Roundabout*
11 *The A Team*
12 *Porridge*
13 *M.A.S.H.*
14 *The Sweeney*

15 *It Ain't Half Hot, Mum*
16 *The Practice*
17 *Hi-de-Hi!*
18 *Terrahawks*
19 *Star Trek*
20 *The Cop And The Kid*

WHO AM I DESCRIBING?

1 Prunella Scales
2 Fay Weldon
3 Orson Welles
4 Brian Walden
5 Susannah York
6 Ludovic Kennedy
7 Richard Stilgoe
8 Esther Rantzen
9 Farrah Fawcett-Majors
10 Freddie Starr
11 Colin Welland
12 Lena Zavaroni
13 Siân Phillips
14 Ian Carmichael
15 Val Doonican

FILL IN THE SPACE

1 Willie
2 *The Incredible Hulk*
3 Pinky and Perky
4 Pugsley and Wednesday
5 *Steptoe And Son*
6 Robert Stack
7 Los Angeles
8 Oracle
9 *Fantasy Island*
10 Lurch

CHILDREN ONLY

1 *What's Happening*
2 *Hold Tight*
3 Mike Read
4 *Murphy's Mob*
5 Telly Buff
6 Dylan
7 Inspector Gadget
8 *Dangermouse*
9 *Tickle On The Tum*
10 Yogi Bear
11 Kermit
12 Tucker Jenkins. The programme was called *Tucker's Luck.*
13 Jimmy and Ian
14 Spinach
15 *Terrahawks*
16 Toronto, Canada
17 Matthew Corbett
18 *Mork And Mindy*
19 *Wacky Races*
20 *Chish 'n' Fips*

IN COMMON

1 They were all written by Carla Lane.
2 The actress Kathy Staff. She plays Doris Luke in *Crossroads* and Nora Batty in *Last Of The Summer Wine.*
3 They have all played the prison governor in *Within These Walls.*

4 They were both written by Alan Bleasdale.

5 Christopher Biggins is a presenter on both of these programmes.

6 They are both newsreaders.

7 Peter Bowles stars in both programmes.

8 They have compered *Sunday Night At The London Palladium*.

9 They both play Detective Inspectors in television police series. John Thaw plays Detective Inspector Regan in *The Sweeney* and Jill Gascoigne plays Detective Inspector Forbes in *The Gentle Touch*.

10 They are all set in Australia.

11 They have all played Dr Who.

12 They all starred Ronnie Corbett and Ronnie Barker.

13 They were all *Charlie's Angels*.

14 They are all actors who star in the zany comedy *Soap*.

15 They both involve computers.

CAN YOU IDENTIFY THE ACTOR?

1	Arthur Lowe	**11**	Stephanie Beacham
2	Richard Beckinsale	**12**	Wilfred Pickles
3	Dennis Weaver	**13**	Arthur Mullard
4	Lorne Greene	**14**	Robert Wagner
5	Gordon Jackson	**15**	Reg Varney
6	Nicholas Lyndhurst	**16**	Paula Wilcox
7	Sir John Mills	**17**	David Janssen
8	Adam West	**18**	Anthony Valentine
9	Patrick McGoohan	**19**	Patrick Wymark
10	Richard O'Sullivan	**20**	Robert Vaughn

OCCUPATIONS

1	Bet Lynch	Barmaid	*Coronation Street*
2	George Jackson	Fireman	*Brookside*
3	Timothy Lumsden	Librarian	*Sorry*
4	Stacy	Policewoman	*T. J. Hooker*
5	Ted Bovis	Comedian	*Hi-de-Hi!*
6	Maggie Forbes	Detective Inspector	*The Gentle Touch*
7	Jim Bergerac	Detective	*Bergerac*
8	Brabinger	Butler	*To The Manor Born*
9	Matt Skilbeck	Farmer	*Emmerdale Farm*
10	Doris Luke	Cleaner	*Crossroads*

11 Mrs Slocombe	Shop Assistant	*Are You Being Served?*
12 Latka	Motor Mechanic	*Taxi*
13 Major Sinclair Yeates	Resident Magistrate	*The Irish R.M.*
14 Michael Ranson	Surgeon	*Falcon Crest*
15 Tracy Willoughby	Nurse	*Angels*

TELEVISION QUIZZES

1 Derek Batey
2 Magnus Magnusson
3 David Coleman
4 Robert Robinson
5 Bamber Gascoigne
6 Paul Daniels
7 Eamonn Andrews
8 Hughie Green
9 Richard Stilgoe
10 Max Bygraves or Bob Monkhouse (both have hosted *Family Fortunes*)

CAN YOU IDENTIFY THE ACTOR 2?

1 Donald Sinden
2 Penelope Keith
3 James Bolam
4 Brian Wilde
5 George Cole
6 Leonard Rossiter
7 Julia McKenzie
8 Mollie Sugden
9 Keith Baron
10 Diane Keen

SPOT THE MISTAKE

1 It is Leonard not Thomas who tempts Ria with his romantic ploys. Thomas is Leonard's chauffeur and confidant.
2 Vince's surname is Pinner. It is Penny who has the surname Warrender.
3 It is Paul Young who sings the theme tune for *Father's Day*.
4 It was Keith Barron who played Daniel Ford.
5 Bill Owen plays Compo in *Last Of The Summer Wine*. Brian Wilde plays Foggy.
6 Tom and Barbara's surname is Good, not Goodwin.
7 The fictitious prison in *Porridge* is Slade prison.
8 Del not Dan is one of the central characters of *Only Fools And Horses*.
9 It was Barry Evans who played the unfortunate teacher in *Mind Your Language*.
10 The series was called *Take A Letter Mr Jones*.

11 Rodney Bewes played Bob in *The Likely Lads*, it was James Bolam who played Terry.
12 *It Ain't Half Hot Mum* is set in India not Korea.
13 Wilfred Brambell and Harry H Corbett played father and son in the long-running comedy series *Steptoe And Son*.
14 It was *Bootsie And Snudge* starring Alfie Bass and Bill Fraser which was a spin-off from *The Army Game*, not *Dad's Army*.
15 Trevor and Vera's surname is Botting, not Brown.
16 *Never Mind The Quality, Feel The Width* concerned a tailoring business, not a joinery business.
17 The comedy which starred Sally Thomsett and Paula Wilcox sharing a flat with Richard O'Sullivan was *Man About The House*. *Robin's Nest* was a spin-off series.
18 It was David Cassidy who starred in *The Partridge Family*, not Donny Osmond.
19 It was Derek Nimmo who played the curate in *All Gas And Gaiters, Oh Brother* and *Oh Father*.
20 Nyree Dawn Porter and Paul Daneman starred in the comedy series *Never A Cross Word*. It was Donald Sinden and Windsor Davies who starred in *Never The Twain*.

HOW WELL DO YOU KNOW YOUR SOAPS?

1 Amos Brearley and Henry Wilks are the landlords of The Woolpack in *Emmerdale Farm*.
2 Angela Channing, the matriarch of Falcon Crest has two daughters, Emma and Julia.
3 Rita Fairclough, a one time nightclub singer owns The Kabin a small newsagents in Coronation Street.
4 Fallon Carrington decided her life was boring and empty so her father gave her a hotel to manage which she named La Mirage.
5 Clive Hornby and Helen Weir, a married couple in real life, play Pat and Jack Sugden in *Emmerdale Farm*.
6 Ken Barlow gave up his job at the community centre and became the editor of The Weatherfield Recorder.
7 The comedy programme *Soap* parodies all soap operas and centres on the lives of two families, the Tates and the Campbells.
8 Jessica Montford was the aristocratic sister of Clayton Farlow.
9 Seth Armstrong is the poacher-turned-gamekeeper in *Emmerdale Farm*.

10 Christopher is the adopted son of Pam and Bobby Ewing.

11 The Rev Donald Hinton, the vicar of Beckindale attempts to bring his village flock together in harmony.

12 *Knot's Landing* was a spin-off series from Dallas which featured Gary the black sheep of the Ewing family.

13 Mia Farrow and Ryan O'Neal were stars in the sixties soap opera *Peyton Place*.

14 Barry, Karen and Damon are the elder children in the Grant household in Brookside Close.

15 *The Groves* was the first real soap opera in Britain which starred Nancy Roberts as a testy old matriarch.

16 The Scottish soap opera *Take The High Road* is set around the fictitious highland community of Glendarrock.

17 *Crossroads*, which was first transmitted in 1964 was originally known as *Midland Road*.

18 The Tilsley's live at number five Coronation Street.

19 The early sixties soap opera *Compact* was set in the offices of a woman's magazine.

20 *Flamingo Road* was based on a book by Robert Wilder.

THE COMEDIANS

1 Arthur Askey
2 Tommy Cooper
3 Max Bygraves
4 Ken Dodd
5 Charlie Drake
6 Hilda Baker
7 Larry Grayson
8 Ronnie Barker and Ronnie Corbett
9 Bruce Forsyth
10 Michael Crawford
11 Harry H Corbett
12 Bernard Bresslaw
13 Peter Cook
14 Bob Monkhouse
15 Dick Emery

POLICE

1 Haskins — *The Sweeney*
2 Detective Chief Inspector Bill Russell — *The Gentle Touch*
3 Detective Inspector Galloway — *The Bill*
4 Officer Dibble — *Top Cat*
5 Inspector Barlow — *Z Cars*
6 Inspector Kate Longton — *Juliet Bravo*

7	Romano	*T. J. Hooker*
8	Sheriff Rosco Coltrane	*The Dukes Of Hazzard*
9	Stavros	*Kojak*
10	Captain Furillo	*Hill Street Blues*

TELEVISION CLASSICS

1	a	Cathy Gale	Honor Blackman
	b	Emma Peel	Diana Rigg
	c	Tara King	Linda Thorson
	d	Purdy	Joanna Lumley

2	Muffin The Mule	11 Alf Garnett's wife Elsie in *Till Death Us Do Part.*
3	Roger Moore and Tony Curtis	12 Victor Sylvester
4	John Drake	13 Lonely
5	*The Man From U.N.C.L.E.*	14 David Carradine
6	Frank Windsor	15 *Star Trek.* Mr Spock
7	*Special Branch*	16 Richard Chamberlain
8	*Juke Box Jury*	17 *Opportunity Knocks*
9	Maigret	18 *The Virginian*
10	The Daleks	19 Batman
		20 Michael Miles

TITLE ROLES

1	*Nanny*	Wendy Craig
2	*The District Nurse*	Nerys Hughes
3	*Bergerac*	John Nettles
4	*Wonderwoman*	Lynda Carter
5	*The Duchess Of Duke Street*	Gemma Jones
6	*Mitch*	John Thaw
7	*Robin Of Sherwood*	Michael Praed
8	*Scully*	Andrew Scofield
9	*Sharon And Elsie*	Janette Beverly and Brigit Forsyth
10	*Shine On Harvey Moon*	Kenneth Cranham
11	*Alice*	Linda Lavin
12	*Hardcastle And McCormick*	Brian Keith and Daniel Hugh-Kelly
13	*Jemima Shore Investigates*	Patricia Hodge
14	*Quincy*	Jack Klugman
15	*Cagney And Lacey*	Sharon Gless and Tyne Daly
16	*The Black Adder*	Rowan Atkinson

17	*The Magnificent Evans*	Ronnie Barker
18	*Rhoda*	Valerie Harper
19	*Reggie*	Richard Mulligan
20	*Robin's Nest*	Richard O'Sullivan

TWENTY QUESTIONS

1	Roy Plomley	**11**	June Whitfield
2	Freddy Grisewood	**12**	Ian McDougall
3	Stuart Hall	**13**	John Peel
4	Robert Fox	**14**	Gloria Hunniford
5	Roy Hudd	**15**	Charlie Chester
6	Mark Page	**16**	Luxembourg
7	Kenny Everett	**17**	Phil Archer
8	Lenny Henry	**18**	Christopher Martin Jenkins
9	Andy Peebles	**19**	Jeremy Beadle
10	Brian Johnston	**20**	Tony Blackburn

RADIO PRESENTERS

1	Sue MacGregor	*Woman's House*
2	Derek Cooper	*The Food Programme*
3	Andy Peebles	*My Top Ten*
4	Barry Norman	*The Chip Shop*
5	Jimmy Savile	*Jimmy Savile's Old Record Club*
6	Alistair Cooke	*Letter From America*
7	Tim Gudgin and Paddy Feany	*Top Of The Form*
8	Louise Botting	*Money Box*
9	Nigel Rees	*Quote . . . Unquote*
10	Jimmy Young	*The Night Is Young*

BREAKFAST TEASER

The following names are all to be found in the Breakfast Teaser.

1	Glynn Christian	**9**	Roddy Llewellyn
2	Frank Bough	**10**	Nick Owen
3	Wincey Willis	**11**	Bob Wilson
4	Mad Lizzie	**12**	Russell Grant
5	Lynn Faulds Wood	**13**	Green Goddess
6	Mike Smith	**14**	Selina Scott
7	Dr Richard Smith	**15**	David Frost
8	Jeni Barnett		

☆ ☆ ☆ ☆ ☆ **BONUS TIME** ☆ ☆ ☆ ☆ ☆

1 *Murder In The Cathedral*
2 *The Six Million Dollar Man*
3 Beat The Clock
4 Iain Cuthbertson
5 *On The Move*
6 Susan Penhaligon
7 *Survival*
8 Nicholas Freeling
9 Edward Fox
10 *Fame*
11 *The Waltons*
12 Nicholas Parsons
13 Sir Mortimer Wheeler
14 *Paperback Writer* by The Beatles
15 Carol White
16 Shula, Kenton, David and Elizabeth
17 *Checkpoint*
18 *It's That Man Again* (also known by its initials ITMA)
19 **a** Harry Secombe
   b Spike Milligan
   c Peter Sellers
20 *The Ying Tong Song*

ADVERTISEMENTS

1 Smarties
2 Mackeson
3 Flora margarine
4 Fresh cream cakes
5 Schweppes
6 Midland Bank
7 Andrex toilet tissue
8 Stork margarine
9 Eggs
10 Milk
11 Heinz baked beans
12 Sarsons vinegar
13 Pye
14 Kodak
15 Nescafé

ODD ONE OUT

1 Miss Jones is the odd one out. A character called Miss Jones appears in *Rising Damp*. Shorofsky, Doris and Bruno Martelli are all characters from *Fame*.
2 Joss Holland is the odd one out. Rose Millar, Blanche and Christina Campbell are all characters from *Tenko*. There was a Joss Holbrook (but not Holland) in the series.
3 Benny Hunter is the odd one out. Mavis Hooper, Jill Chance and Miranda Pollard are characters from *Crossroads*. Benny in *Crossroads* is Benny Hawkins.
4 Mr Grouse is the odd one out. Fred Quilly, Ted Bovis and Sylvia are all characters from *Hi-de-Hi!*

5 Uncle Jester is the odd one out. Daisy, Enos and Boss Hogg are all characters from *The Dukes Of Hazzard*. The uncle in *The Dukes Of Hazzard* is called Uncle Jesse.

6 Margaret Frogerty is the odd one out. Mrs Polouvicka, Ned and Richard De Vere are all characters from *To The Manor Born*.

7 Stewpot Stevens is the odd one out. Claire Scott, Zammo and Mr Browning are all characters from *Grange Hill*. Stewpot in *Grange Hill* is Stewpot Stewart.

8 Suzanne is the odd one out. Hannibal, Murdock and Baracus are all characters from *The A Team*.

9 Simon Forbes is the odd one out. Detective Sergeant Jake Barratt, Detective Sergeant Peter Phillips, Detective Inspector Mike Turnbull are all characters from *The Gentle Touch*. Steve Forbes, not Simon Forbes, is the character in the series.

10 Maggie Channing is the odd one out. Angela Channing, Lance and Chase Gioberti are all characters from *Falcon Crest*. Maggie in *Falcon Crest* is Maggie Gioberti.

COMPLETE THE LINE

1 *Chips*
2 *Opportunity Knocks*
3 Isla St Clair
4 *The Liver Birds*
5 Seaton
6 Yosser
7 Waring (Eddie Waring)
8 Hudson
9 *Yes Minister*
10 Nicholson (Viv Nicholson)

WHERE DID I HEAR THAT?????????

1 Alan Freeman
2 Radio programme *Week Ending*
3 Jimmy Young
4 The opening lines of *Listen With Mother*
5 Jimmy Savile
6 Walter Gabriel in the long-running radio soap opera *The Archers*
7 John Timson's closing words on *Today*
8 Terry Wogan's phrase for getting rid of excess weight.
9 The dog on Tony Blackburn's programme, who frequently interrupts with his 'Woof-woof'.
10 A Cockney voice on Ed Stewart's radio show.

SELECT ONE

1 b   6 b
2 a   7 a
3 c   8 c
4 c   9 b
5 c   10 b

FILL IN THE SPACES

1 Michael Bentine   6 Simon Bates
2 *Hancock's*   7 Anne Nightingale
3 Dave Lee Travis   8 Gordon Clough
4 Janice Long   9 Nelson
5 *Touch*   10 2

CARTOON CHARACTERS

1 Mr McGoo   6 Fred Flintstone
2 Speedy Gonzales   7 Pink Panther
3 Road Runner   8 Tweety Pie
4 Yogi Bear   9 Jerry
5 Dangermouse   10 Tom

NEWSREADERS

1 Richard Baker   8 John Timpson
2 Michael Aspel   9 Cliff Michelmore (He married
3 *That's Life Newsdesk*   Jean Metcalf who introduced
4 Gerald Seymour   the London end of *Family*
5 Trevor McDonald   *Favourites* while he presented
6 Robert Dougal   the German end)
7 Simon Bates   10 Selina Scott

DISC JOCKEYS

1 Dave Lee Travis   6 Jimmy Young
2 Kenny Everett   7 Steve Wright
3 Noel Edmonds   8 David Hamilton
4 Paul Gambaccini   9 David Jensen
5 Paul Burnett   10 Stuart Henry

CORONATION STREET

1 Patricia Phoenix
2 Jack Smethurst
3 Martha Longhurst
4 Concepta Riley
5 Gordon Clegg
6 Tracy Lynette Langton
7 Susan and Peter
8 She was electrocuted by a faulty hair-dryer plug
9 Renee Roberts
10 Ivan Cheveski
11 Maggie Dunlop
12 He owns a car repair garage
13 Len Fairclough
14 The Ogdens
15 Annie Walker
16 Whisky
17 Bet Lynch
18 Ena Sharples
19 Jerry Booth
20 Marion Willis

IT'S A LAUGH

1 Father and son
2 Jerry and Margo Leadbeatter
3 *Love Thy Neighbour*
4 Tristram
5 *Private Benjamin*
6 Betty
7 Tommy Cannon and Bobby Ball
8 Irene Handl
9 *That's My Boy*
10 *Duty Free*
11 *Young At Heart*
12 *Up Pompeii*
13 David Copperfield
14 Popeye
15 *Poor Little Rich Girls*
16 Patrick Cargill
17 Governor Gatling
18 Dr Evadne Hinge and Dame Hilda Bracket
19 *Hi-de-Hi!*
20 Morgenstern

HOW WELL DO YOU KNOW YOUR SOAPS 2?

1 Newton and Ridley
2 Heather Huntington (maiden name Haversham)
3 Sally Waterman
4 Adam
5 Donna
6 Glenda Banks
7 *Falcon Crest*
8 Tool hire business
9 Terry Wogan
10 *Queen Victoria*
11 He does not speak
12 Kevin and Debbie
13 Jane Wyman
14 King's Oak
15 Kirby Anders

16 Jenna Wade
17 Percy Sugden
18 Elizabeth Cunningham
19 Curly Watts
20 John Ross

FILL IN THE BLANKS

1 Bill Beaumont and Emlyn Hughes
2 *Ultra Quiz*
3 *Blockbusters*
4 *Vintage Quiz*. Lord Montagu of Beaulieu
5 101 in 6 darts
6 Monica Rose
7 *University Challenge*
8 Max Bygraves, Bob Monkhouse
9 Julian Pettifer
10 *Where In The World*
11 Maggie Moon, Kaluki
12 Tom O'Connor
13 *The Price Is Right*
14 Michael Miles
15 *Where In The World*

TWENTY QUESTIONS

1 Robby Box
2 David and Amy Pearce
3 Marti Caine
4 *Ever Decreasing Circles*
5 *Dear Ladies*
6 *Star Trek*
7 *McCloud*
8 Peter Skellern
9 Railway Terrace
10 *The Champions*
11 Thora Hird
12 Hartley Police Station
13 A jet-black turbo motor-cycle
14 Mike Yarwood
15 Bruce Forsyth's *Play Your Cards Right*.

TV PERSONALITIES

1 Sue Nicholls
2 Eamonn Andrews
3 Barbara Woodhouse
4 Tom O'Connor
5 Jan Leeming
6 Russell Harty
7 Peter Davison
8 Noel Edmonds
9 Judith Hann
10 Maureen Lipman
11 Bill Maynard
12 Mary Parkinson
13 Esther Rantzen
14 Terry Scott
15 Roger De Courcey

TELEVISION FEATURES

1 *This Is Your Life*
2 *Razzmatazz*
3 Points make prizes
4 Noel Edmond's *Late Late Breakfast Show*
5 Ernie Wise
6 Tonto said this to The Lone Ranger
7 *Paul Daniel's Magic Show*
8 Arthur Daley in *Minder*
9 *Blockbusters*
10 *Steptoe And Son*
11 *On Safari*
12 Lorraine Chase
13 Kenny Everett
14 *The Muppet Show*
15 Frank Spencer, played by Michael Crawford in *Some Mothers Do Have 'Em*

CROSSROADS

1 Malcolm Ryder
2 Vince Parker
3 Sarah Jane
4 Hairdresser
5 Ronald Allen
6 She is a successful novelist
7 Hawkins
8 Chris
9 Father and daughter
10 New York
11 Patricia Hamilton
12 Paul Ross
13 In a car accident
14 Joe MacDonald
15 Hugh Mortimer

TELEVISION CHARACTERS

1 *Starsky And Hutch*
2 *The A Team*
3 *T. J. Hooker*
4 *Yes, Minister*
5 *Hill Street Blues*
6 *Airwolf*
7 *Me And My Girl*
11 *Night Court*
12 *Tenko*
13 *Cheers*
14 *The Gentle Touch*
15 *The Addams Family*
16 *Auf Wiedersehen, Pet*
17 *Barney Miller*

8 *Bewitched*

9 *The Yellow Rose*

10 *Brookside*

18 *To The Manor Born*

19 *Bergerac*

20 *One By One*

How well did you do?

Maximum score 660. If you scored more than 250 – give yourself a pat on the back; more than 350 – open a bottle of champagne; over 450 – you should be a TV producer, or perhaps you already are one.

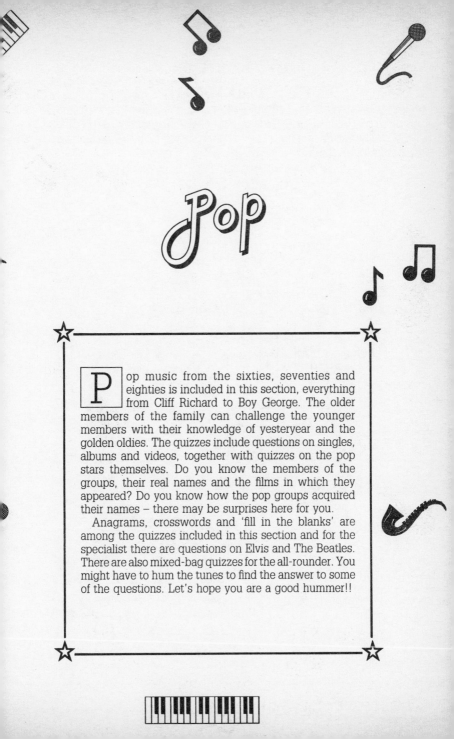

Pop

Pop music from the sixties, seventies and eighties is included in this section, everything from Cliff Richard to Boy George. The older members of the family can challenge the younger members with their knowledge of yesteryear and the golden oldies. The quizzes include questions on singles, albums and videos, together with quizzes on the pop stars themselves. Do you know the members of the groups, their real names and the films in which they appeared? Do you know how the pop groups acquired their names – there may be surprises here for you.

Anagrams, crosswords and 'fill in the blanks' are among the quizzes included in this section and for the specialist there are questions on Elvis and The Beatles. There are also mixed-bag quizzes for the all-rounder. You might have to hum the tunes to find the answer to some of the questions. Let's hope you are a good hummer!!

VIDEO WORDS

For ten points can you complete the columns using the clues given, which all relate to top-selling pop videos? On completing the VIDEO WORDS you will find in the highlighted squares, the name of the first promotional video by a particular band.

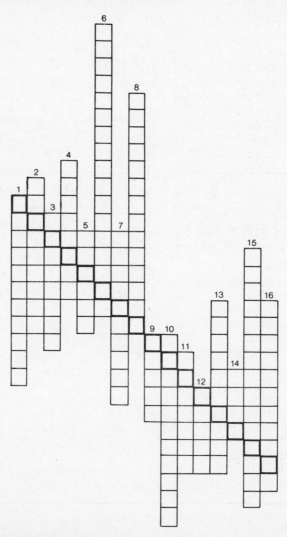

SOLUTIONS ON PAGE 109

CLUES

1 'Smalltown Boy' brought them success.
2 A US/Russian fight for Frankie Goes To Hollywood.
3 Best selling video by Michael Jackson.
4 Wham's request before you leave.
5 His was a 'Never Ending Story'.
6 A request from ZZ Top.
7 Boy George sang '. . . and people are stupid'.
8 He sang about 'Billie Jean'.
9 A request from Frankie Goes To Hollywood.
10 He could be described as 'Hyperactive'.
11 'Wings Of A Dove' was a hit for them.
12 U2 were pleased with this video.
13 Who asked 'Wouldn't It Be Good?'
14 Their's was a 'Labour Of Love'
15 A video hit for Elton.
16 Simon Le Bon was strapped to a windmill for this video.

SCORE 10 POINTS

CAN YOU IDENTIFY THE FOLLOWING GROUPS?

Below are listed some of the members of well-known groups. Can you identify them?

1 John Taylor, Andy Taylor
2 Keren, Siobhan, Sarah
3 Peter Tork, Mickey Dolenz
4 Paul Di'Anno, Steve Harris, Dave Murray
5 Thomas McClary, Walter Orange, Ronald LaPread
6 Jon Moss
7 Gary Kemp, Steve Norman
8 Mike Nolan, Jay Aston
9 David Jaymes, Michael Mullins, Robbie Jaymes
10 George Anderson, Gill Saward, Keith Winter
11 Mickey Virtue, Brian Travers, Jimmy Brown
12 Stewart Copeland
13 Benn Watt, Tracy Thorn
14 Daniel Woodgate, Lee Thompson, Chris Foreman
15 Frank Maudsley

SCORE 15 POINTS

SOLUTIONS ON PAGE 109

SOLO ARTISTS

Can you identify the solo artists who sang the following songs?

1 'Are Friends Electric', 'Complex', 'We Take Mystery'. Was it Paul Young, Gary Numan, Julian Lennon or David Bowie?

2 'Sunglasses', 'Helpless', 'Move Over Darling'. Was it Janet Jackson, Chaka Khan, Tracey Ullman or Cyndi Lauper?

3 'Watching The Detectives', 'Pump It Up', 'Radio, Radio'. Was it Neil Young, Elvis Costello, Limahl or Kim Wilde?

4 'Eighth Day', 'D-Days', 'Will You'. Was it Hazel O'Connor, Suzi Quatro, Kiki Dee or Hazell Dean?

5 'Oh Julie', 'Shirley', 'I'll Be Satisfied'. Was it Gary Glitter, Shakin' Stevens, Jermaine Jackson or Phil Lynott?

6 'Kids In America', 'Water On Glass', 'View From A Bridge'. Was it Alison Moyet, Gloria Gaynor, Kim Wilde or Tina Turner?

SOLUTIONS ON PAGE 109

7 'Rock With You', 'One Day In Your Life', 'We're Almost There'. Was it Michael Jackson, David Bowie, Gary Numan or Paul McCartney?

8 'I'm Gonna Tear Your Playhouse Down', 'Everything Must Change', 'Wherever I Lay My Hat (That's My Home)'. Was it Billy Idol, Divine, Paul Young or David Sylvian?

9 'Like To Get To Know You Well', 'New Song', 'Pearl In The Shell'. Was it Howard Jones, Limahl, George Michael or Feargal Sharkey?

10 'Dress You Up', 'Borderline', 'Like A Virgin'. Was it Tracie, Madonna, Stephanie Mills or Helen Terry?

11 'Let The Music Play', 'Give Me Tonight', 'Sweet Somebody'. Was it Deniece Williams, Laura Brannigan, Shannon or Cyndi Lauper?

12 'Pulling Punches', 'The Ink In The Well', 'Red Guitar'. Was it David Sylvian, Captain Sensible, Divine or David Austin?

13 'Invisible', 'All Cried Out', 'Love Resurrection'. Was it Hazell Dean, Carol Kenyan, Nena or Alison Moyet?

14 'I Feel Like Buddy Holly', 'So Near To Christmas', 'I Won't Run Away'. Was it Ian McCulloch, John Waite, Alvin Stardust or Gary Glitter?

15 '48 Crash', 'Daytona Demon', 'The Race Is On'. Was it Kiki Dee, Gerry Rafferty, Suzi Quatro or Julie Covington?

SCORE 15 POINTS

NO. ONE HIT ALBUMS

All of the LPs below reached No. one in the pop charts. Can you unscramble the letters to reveal the recording artists?

1 *Atlantic Crossing* (1975)   RT WESTROAD
2 *Rumours* (1977)   WOOLFACT DEEM
3 *Avalon* (1982)   SIX COY RUM

SOLUTIONS ON PAGE 110

4	*Fog On The Tyne* (1971)	DANIEL FIRNS
5	*Love Over Gold* (1982)	IS IT A REST, DR
6	*Telekon* (1980)	A GRUM NANY
7	*Arrival* (1976)	BABA
8	*Venus And Mars* (1975)	SWING
9	*The Number Of The Beast* (1982)	MOIRA DENIN
10	*No Sleep Till Hammersmith* (1981)	O DEAR MOTH
11	*Face Value* (1981)	PLONI CHILLS
12	*Pot Luck* (1962)	YES REVEL LIPS
13	*Ooh-La-La* (1973)	CHAT FEES
14	*Never For Ever* (1980)	BAKE HUTS
15	*Abacab* (1981)	NESSIGE

SCORE 15 POINTS

POP FACTS

Can you say True or False to each of the following statements?

1 True or False? An Australian sang the Irish entry to the 1980 Eurovision Song Contest.

SOLUTIONS ON PAGE 110

2 True or False? Mike Batt was the voice behind The Wombles and also had a hit with 'Summertime City'.

3 True or False? In 1980 John Lennon was awarded a rhodium-plated disc for being history's all-time best selling songwriter and recording artist.

4 True or False? Rod Stewart's first No. one hit single in 1971 was 'Maggie May'.

5 True or False? The band Musical Youth originated from Manchester.

6 Elvis Presley earned 28 gold discs in his lifetime.

7 'Amazing Grace', 'Don't Cry For Me Argentina' and 'Annie's Song' have all reached the top ten in both vocal and instrumental versions.

8 David 'Kid' Jensen became Europe's youngest disc jockey when he joined Radio Luxembourg in 1968.

SOLUTIONS ON PAGE 110

9 Jimi Hendrix and Cher had one thing in common, they were both part Cherokee Indian.

10 Elton John is associated with Brentford Football Club.

11 True or False? Sir Ralph Richardson appeared in Paul McCartney's film, *Give My Regards To Broad Street*.

12 Jim Reeves recorded the first posthumous No. one hit record.

13 *The Official BBC Album Of The Royal Wedding* reached No. one in the pop LP charts in 1980.

14 True or False? The BBC banned Duran Duran's 'Relax' song in 1984.

15 Marty and Kim Wilde are brother and sister.

SCORE 15 POINTS

POP STARS, FILMS AND THEME MUSIC

Many pop stars become involved in films, either acting or composing music. Can you answer the following questions which concern this subject?

1 For which film did Art Garfunkel compose the song 'Bright Eyes'?

2 What are the names of the two rival groups in *Purple Rain*?

3 What was the title of the 1969 film which featured the folk singer Arlo Guthrie on the verge of being drafted?

4 Which Australian outlaw did Mick Jagger play in the 1970 film of the same name?

5 On which gospel was the musical *Godspell* based?

6 Whose life story was told in the film *Lady Sings The Blues*?

7 Which American female vocalist sang the theme song from the

SOLUTIONS ON PAGE 110

controversial film *Soldier Blue* (1971)?

8 Which Beatle turned film producer for Monty Python's film *Life Of Brian*?

9 What was the title of the hit single from the soundtrack of the film *McVicar*?

10 Which film of 1980 starred Hazel O'Connor in the story of a punk band's rise and fall?

11 Who recorded the theme music for the film *1984*?

12 Who sang the title song from the scary comedy film *Ghostbusters*?

13 Which pop singer played the Acid Queen in Ken Russell's film *Tommy*?

14 Who sang 'Remember My Name', the title tune of the film *Fame* (1982)?

15 Which pouting pop star performs in the 1984 film *Purple Rain*?

SCORE 15 POINTS

ALSO KNOWN AS ...

Pop stars often change their names (often more than once) to suit their pop images. Can you identify the following singers, some old, some new?

1 Vincent Furnier
2 Stuart Goddard
3 Richard Penniman
4 William Robinson
5 Cherilyn Sarkasia LaPier
6 James Marcus Smith
7 Harry Rodger Webb
8 Donna Gaines
9 Francis Avallone
10 Prince Rogers Nelson
11 Declan McManus
12 Concetta Franconero
13 Mark Feld
14 Gary Webb
15 George O'Dowd

SCORE 15 POINTS

SOLUTIONS ON PAGE 111

ALL SORTS

Can you complete the sentences by filling in the blank spaces?

1 *Inflammable Material* (1979) was the debut album of the punk band _____ _____ _____.

2 Limahl was a member of _____ before launching his solo career.

3 John Lennon's original middle name was _____. He later changed it to Ono.

4 _____ had a Christmas hit in 1973 with 'I Wish It Could Be Christmas Everyday'.

5 Lonnie Donegan sang 'My Old Man's a _____' in 1960.

6 _____ _____ of Duran Duran married Julie Anne Friedman on 18 August 1984.

7 Fleetwood Mac had a hit in 1969 with the instrumental _____.

8 The _____ _____ sang about 'Anarchy In The UK' (1976).

9 *Brilliant Trees* (1984) was a top selling album for _____ _____.

10 *The Other Side Of The Tracks* is a television programme presented by _____ _____.

11 'Ease On Down The Road' is a duet by Diana Ross and _____ _____.

12 _____ _____ plays May Day in the Bond Movie, *From A View To A Kill*.

13 'Caroline', 'Dirty Water' and 'Paper Plane' are all classics from _____ _____.

14 *Make It Big* is an album by _____.

15 *Dune* (1984) is a science fiction film epic featuring _____.

SCORE 15 POINTS

SOLUTIONS ON PAGE 111

POP DUOS

Can you complete the singing duos for the following songs?

1 'All Of You' (1984) — Julio Iglesias and _____ _____

2 'Endless Love' (1981) — Diana Ross and _____ _____

3 'Surf City' (1963) — Jan and _____

4 'Hold Me' (1981) — B.A. Robertson and _____ _____

5 'In The Year 2525' (1969) — Zager and _____

6 'Summer Nights' (1978) — John Travolta and _____ _____ _____

7 'It's My Party' (1981) — Dave Stewart and _____ _____

8 'Something Stupid' (1967) — Frank and _____ _____

9 'I Got You Babe' (1965) — Sonny and _____

10 'She's Gone' (1976) — Daryl Hall and _____ _____

11 'Ain't No Pleasing You' (1982) — Chas and _____

SOLUTIONS ON PAGE 111

12 'We All Stand Together'   Paul McCartney and _____
(1984)   _____ _____

13 'You Don't Bring Me   Barbra Streisand and _____
Flowers' (1978)   _____

14 'You're All I Need To   Johnny Mathis and _____ _____
Get By' (1978)

15 'Mockingbird' (1974)   Carly Simon and _____ _____

SCORE 15 POINTS

ELVIS

Elvis Presley was in the pop charts for more than twenty years and his music and style influenced a generation. How well did you know Elvis?

1 In which town was Elvis born?

2 Elvis was very close to his mother and was heartbroken when she died in 1958. What was his mother's name?

3 What was Elvis' first No. one hit single of 1957?

4 Elvis Presley made his television debut on a show with two Big Band brothers. Who were they?

5 What was the title of Elvis' first film?

6 What was the name of Elvis' 23 room mansion?

7 Which film was Elvis working on when he received his draft notice?

8 Who did Elvis marry on 1 May 1967?

9 What is the name of Presley's only daughter?

10 In which year did Elvis die?

11 What was Elvis' middle name?

12 Which Elvis record was the first record since the beginning of the British pop charts to enter at No. one?

13 'Wooden Heart' was a popular No. one hit from Elvis. This song was featured in which film?

SOLUTIONS ON PAGE 112

14 What was on the other side of Elvis' No. one 'Rock-A-Hula Baby'?

15 What was Elvis' final No. one of 1977 which remained in the charts for five weeks?

SCORE 15 POINTS

GOLDEN OLDIES

Some pop records retain their popularity despite their age. Can you complete the blanks in the following golden oldies?

1	'I _____'	Frankie Laine
2	'_____ Around _____ _____'	Bill Haley And His Comets
3	'Three _____ _____ _____'	Eddie Cochran
4	'_____ Laura _____ _____ _____'	Ricky Valance
5	'_____ Be _____ _____'	The Crickets
6	'_____ _____'	Danny Williams
7	'Why _____ _____ _____ _____ _____'	Frankie Lymon And The Teenagers
8	'You'll _____ _____ _____'	Gerry And The Pacemakers
9	'_____ Rock'	Elvis Presley
10	'_____ All _____'	Johnny Kidd And The Pirates

SCORE 10 POINTS

INSTRUMENTS

1 Who played virtually all 28 instruments on the Number One LP *Tubular Bells*?

2 Who played lead guitar on The Beatles record 'Ticket To Ride'?

3 Who plays the synthesizer in Duran Duran?

4 Which Asian instrument was featured on The Beatles 1965 song 'Norwegian Wood'?

SOLUTIONS ON PAGE 112

5 Who is the drummer in Police?

6 The musician who has been called one of the most innovative and influential rock guitarists and the most important electric guitarist after Charlie Christian, began his career as Jimmy James. By what name was he more commonly known?

7 Ann 'Honey' Lantree was a member of The Honeycombs; which instrument did she play?

8 'The Lonely Bull' and 'A Taste Of Honey' were hits for Herb Alpert. What is the instrument associated with him, which he began playing at the age of eight?

9 Which member of Jethro Tull was known for such stage antics as playing the flute while hopping from leg to leg?

10 He won a scholarship to the Royal Academy of Music where he studied for six years before he launched into show business. His albums include *Empty Sky* (1969) and *Captain Fantastic And The Brown Dirt Cowboy* (1975). Who is he and which instrument do you associate with him?

SCORE 10 POINTS

SOLUTIONS ON PAGE 112

IN COMMON

Can you identify something which each of the following have in common?

1 Bob Neal, Scotty Moore and Colonel Tom Parker.

2 Stiff Little Fingers, The Buzzcocks and The Stranglers.

3 'Apache', 'Roulette' and 'Rebel Rouser'.

4 Jimmy Page, Robert Plant, John Bonham and John Paul Jones.

5 *Arrival, Super Trouper* and *The Visitors*.

6 'Secret Love', 'Summer Holiday' and 'You're The One That I Want'.

7 Barry Gibb, Neil Diamond, Donna Summer.

8 The Walker Brothers, The Thompson Twins and The Righteous Brothers.

9 Stevie Wonder, Lenny Peters and Ray Charles.

10 Shirley Bassey, Paul McCartney and Carly Simon.

SCORE 10 POINTS

TRUE OR FALSE?

Are the following statements True or False?

1 True or False? Paul Young led a band called The Royal Family.

2 True or False? Lionel Richie was formerly a member of The Commotions before going solo.

3 True or False? Rod Stewart and Jeff Beck recorded a single called 'I've Been Drinking' (1973).

SOLUTIONS ON PAGE 112

4 True or False? The heavy metal group Rainbow had a top video called *Live Between The Eyes*.

5 True or False? The official biography of Duran Duran is called *When Cameras Go Crazy*.

6 True or False? Divine is a woman.

7 True or False? 'Say, Say, Say' was the title of a duet by Michael Jackson and Diana Ross.

8 True or False? 'China Girl', 'Heroes' and Bowie's 'Sorrow' are all tracks from *Love You Till Tuesday*.

9 True or False? Jools Holland and Leslie Ash presented television's pop programme *Razzmatazz*.

10 True or False? *Human Racing* was the debut album of Carmel.

SCORE 10 POINTS

SOLUTIONS ON PAGE 113

POP STARS AND FILMS

Many pop stars have also turned their talents to the acting profession. Can you name the pop stars who star in the following films?

1 *A Hard Day's Night*
2 *The Young Ones*
3 *Tommy*
4 *Blue Hawaii*
5 *Saturday Night Fever*
6 *Catch Us If You Can*
7 *A Star Is Born*
8 *Order Of Death*
9 *Pat Garret And Billy The Kid*
10 *The Man Who Fell To Earth*
11 *The Wall*
12 *The Jazz Singer*
13 *Lady Sings The Blues*
14 *The Wiz*
15 *Xanadu*

SCORE 15 POINTS

VIDEO, VIDEO

In the eighties videos have become an enhanced way of enjoying music by making it possible to watch the performers as well as listening to their music. Can you unscramble the letters to identify the artists featured on these top pop videos?

1 'Hello Again'   H. T. SCARE
2 'Sing Blue Silver'   NAR DUDU NAR
3 'Highly Strung'   AAU SPELT BLAND
4 'Come Back And Stay'   GAOL PUUNY
5 'Deaf Not Blind'   TOM RHEADO
6 'Smalltown Boy'   BARE SNOB KIT
7 'Stand And Deliver'   TANA DAM
8 'Ashes To Ashes'   IBIDO WAVED
9 'Love Is A Stranger'   RICEY THUMS
10 'A Kiss Across The Ocean' BLURT CLUE CU

SCORE 10 POINTS

SOLUTIONS ON PAGE 114

★★★★★★★★★★★★★★

BONUS QUESTIONS

1 Bob Dylan had four classic top ten hits in Britain in 1965. Can you name them?

2 In which year did Jimi Hendrix die?

3 What was the title of Cliff Richard's first No. one hit which did not feature the Shadows?

4 Between the years 1963 and 1967 The Bachelors had six songs in the charts whose titles contained girls' names. Can you name five of the six songs?

5 What was the title of Joe Dolce's one-hit wonder of 1981?

6 Four record companies turned down The Beatles before they were finally signed by Parlophone. Who were the four who regret their decision?

SOLUTIONS ON PAGE 114

7 'I Could Be So Good For You' reached number three in the British pop charts in 1980. The singer is better known as an actor. Who is he?

8 The television programme *The Tube* won a gold award at the International Film and Television Festival of New York in 1984. It received this award for the thirty-minute documentary of which band?

9 Alvin Stardust invited a young person on *Saturday Superstore* to devise a video for his 1984 Christmas disc. What was the title of the disc?

10 Which member of Led Zeppelin produced a gold solo album called *Pictures At Eleven*?

SCORE 2 POINTS FOR EACH CORRECT ANSWER

THE BEATLES AND AFTER

In these multiple choice questions about this world-famous group choose one answer from those given.

1 The youngest Beatle was
   a John Lennon
   b Paul McCartney
   c Ringo Starr
   d George Harrison

2 Who was the original drummer with The Beatles?
   a Ringo Starr
   b Pete Best
   c Stu Sutcliffe
   d Gerry Marsden

3 What was the name of the club in Liverpool where they played and were discovered by Brian Epstein?
   a The Cellar
   b The Kabin
   c The Cavern
   d The Arches

SOLUTIONS ON PAGE 114

4 In which year did The Beatles first perform before the Queen Mother at the Royal Command Variety Performance?
  a 1965
  b 1964
  c 1963
  d 1962

5 What was the title of The Beatles' first album?
  a *With The Beatles*
  b *A Hard Day's Night*
  c *The Beatles*
  d *Please Please Me*

6 The Beatles debut film was
  a *Sergeant Pepper's Lonely Hearts Club Band*
  b *Yellow Submarine*
  c *A Hard Day's Night*
  d *Help!*

7 The Beatles were awarded MBEs (Member of the Order of the British Empire medals) on 26 October 1969. Who returned his medal later that year?
  a John Lennon
  b Paul McCartney
  c Ringo Starr
  d George Harrison

8 The Beatles gave up touring after a concert in San Francisco's Candlestick Park. In which year was this?
  a 1965
  b 1966
  c 1967
  d 1968

9 What was the name of The Beatles own recording label? Was it
  a Magical Mystery
  b Apple
  c Beatles' Records
  d Liverpool Music

SOLUTIONS ON PAGE 115

10 By what other name was their double album *The Beatles* 1968 also known?
  a *The Collection Album*
  b *The Blue Album*
  c *Greatest Hits*
  d *The White Album*

11 Who wrote 'Something', a song which was covered by many other singers?
  a Paul McCartney
  b Paul McCartney and John Lennon
  c George Harrison
  d Ringo Starr

12 Paul McCartney and his band Wings recorded the title theme song for a James Bond movie. Was it
  a *Thunderball*
  b *Live And Let Die*
  c *Diamonds Are Forever*
  d *You Only Live Twice*

13 Which John Lennon and Yoko Ono album won a Grammy Award in 1981 as the Album of the Year?
  a *Mind Games*
  b *Unfinished Music No.2*
  c *Double Fantasy*
  d *Some Time In New York City*

14 In 1956 George Harrison formed his own group. They were known as
  a The Quarrymen
  b The Silver Beatles
  c The Rebels
  d The Drifters

15 Which former Beatle's autobiography is entitled *I Me Mine*?
  a Paul McCartney
  b Ringo Starr
  c George Harrison
  d John Lennon

SOLUTIONS ON PAGE 115

16 Ringo Starr was the stage name of Richard Starky. How did he acquire the name 'Ringo'?
  a He loved wearing lots of rings
  b It was a nickname from school
  c He used to be scolded for leaving a ring around the bathtub
  d He dreamt it up one day

17 Ringo Starr embarked on a film career after leaving The Beatles. In which film did he make his solo film debut? Was it
  a *That'll Be The Day*
  b *Born To Boogie*
  c *Caveman*
  d *Candy*

18 Who did Paul McCartney sing with on the top ten hit single 'The Girl Is Mine' (1983)?
  a Stevie Wonder
  b Tracy Ullman
  c Michael Jackson
  d Linda McCartney

19 In which year was John Lennon murdered? Was it
  a 1978
  b 1979
  c 1980
  d 1981

20 What is the name of John Lennon and Yoko Ono's son?
  a Jude
  b Julian
  c Shane
  d Sean

SCORE 20 POINTS

LEAD SINGERS AND THEIR GROUPS

Can you name the groups which were associated with the following singers?

  1 Siouxsie And _____ _____

SOLUTIONS ON PAGE 115

2 Ian Dury And ____ ____

3 Echo And ____ ____

4 Geno Washington And ____ ____ ____ ____

5 Elvis Costello And ____ ____

6 Bob Marley And ____ ____

7 Father Abraham And ____ ____

8 Kid Creole And ____ ____

9 The Mamas And ____

10 Sly And ____ ____ ____

SCORE 10 POINTS

POP STARS AND FILMS 2

1 Which band recorded the theme for the Bond movie *A View To A Kill*?

2 Who sings the title song from *Give My Regards To Broad Street* (1984)?

3 The music of which band is featured in the 1982 film *The Wall*?

4 Blondie's hit song 'Call Me' (1980) was taken from which film?

5 John Denver recorded 'Sweet Surrender' which was used for the soundtrack of which Disney film?

6 Which band recorded the soundtrack for *Flash Gordon* (1980)?

7 Which singer turned actor for the films *Brimstone And Treacle* (1982) and *The Bride* (1984)?

8 Which singer/musician won a British Film Award for his role in *Alfie Darling* (1975)?

SOLUTIONS ON PAGE 115

9 Culture Club, Heaven 17, Helen Terry and Phil Oakey provided the music for the soundtrack of which film of 1984?

10 Who was nominated for two Oscars for his music for the 1981 film *Ragtime*?

SCORE 10 POINTS

SINGING THE BLUES

Can you identify the artists who sang these blues songs?

1 'Blue River' (1966)
2 'Bluebottle Blues' (1956)
3 'Blue Is The Colour' (1972)
4 'Blue Turns To Grey' (1966)

5 'Blueberry Hill' (1956 and 1976)
6 'Summertime Blues' (1958 and 1968)
7 'Bluer Than Blue' (1969)
8 'Blue Bayou' (1978)
9 'Jazzin For Blue Jean' (1984)
10 'Blue Angel' (1960)

Cliff Richard
Jonathan King
Linda Ronstadt
Roy Orbison
Elvis Presley
George Michael

Chelsea Football Club
Rolf Harris
David Bowie
The Goons
Fats Domino
Eddie Cochran

SCORE 10 POINTS

SOLUTIONS ON PAGE 116

COMPLETE THE TITLES

Can you complete the titles of the following singles of 1984?

1 'Love's Great _____'   (Ultravox)
2 'I'm Gonna _____ _____
_____ _____'   (Paul Young)

3 'All _____ _____'   (Alison Moyet)
4 '_____ _____
_____ Christmas?'   (Band Aid)
5 'Hotline _____ _____'   (Bananarama)
6 'The _____ _____
_____'   (Limahl)

7 'Too Late _____ _____'   (Julian Lennon)
8 'Do The _____'   (Black Lace)
9 'I'm So _____'   (Divine)
10 'Listen To _____ _____'   (Feargal Sharkey)
11 'All Through _____
_____'   (Cyndi Lauper)

12 'Back In _____ _____'   (Hazell Dean)
13 'We Are _____'   (Sister Sledge)
14 'Never _____ _____'   (Orchestral Manoeuvres In
The Dark)

15 'The Power _____ _____'   (Frankie Goes To Hollywood)

SCORE 15 POINTS

THREE TIMES A LADY

Can you name the artists who sang about the following ladies?

1 Louise (1984)
2 Bernadette (1967 and 1972)
3 Lucille (1957)
4 Eloise (1968)
5 Rose Marie (1955)
6 Cath (1984)
7 Marianne (1968)
8 Madame Butterfly (1984)
9 Peggy Sue (1957 and 1968)
10 Mandy (1975)
11 Joanna (1968)
12 Roxanne (1979)
13 Sandy (1978)
14 Carrie-Anne (1967)
15 Mrs Robinson (1968)

SCORE 15 POINTS

SOLUTIONS ON PAGE 116

SKELETON QUIZ

The first clue gives the central vertical of the puzzle, the others give all the horizontal lines. Once you have answered question one correctly, your task will be much easier.

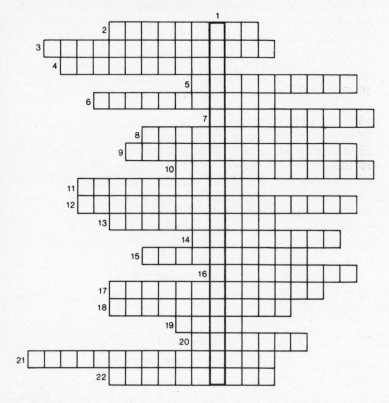

CLUES

1 Collective name of Jill Bryson and Rose McDowell
2 Singer with Cocteau Twins
3 She had phenomenal success with Paul Miles-Kingston with 'Pie Jesu'
4 'Love Is A Battlefield' according to this lady
5 She is a member of The Dream Academy
6 'Knock On Wood' and 'Light My Fire' were old disco favourites by this lady

SOLUTIONS ON PAGE 116

7 Siobhan, Keren and Sarah make up this group
8 She is the girl in Everything But The Girl
9 She had a number one hit with Elaine Page and 'I Know Him So Well'
10 She married Steve Lillywhite, the record producer
11 Known by the nickname Alf
12 Female drummer with Fun Boy 3 and then Everything But The Girl
13 Girl with flowing blonde hair in Shakatak
14 'Invitation To Dance' was one of her singles in 1985
15 The LP *Private Dancer* was a phenomenal success for this soul veteran
16 'This Is My Night' was one of her single releases in 1985
17 Female in Thompson Twins
18 Jay Aston is one of the girls in Bucks Fizz – name the other
19 She played Isla St Porage in television's *Supergran*
20 'Like A Virgin' was very successful for _____ Ciccone
21 *Secrets, Secrets* was an album by this lady in 1985
22 She sang with Culture Club before going solo

SCORE 22 POINTS

ROCK IN THE EIGHTIES

1 The story of which band is told in the book *And Suddenly There Came A Bang* (1985)?

2 What is Stephen Duffy's middle name?

3 Can you name the *Go West* duo?

4 What is the title of the 1985 break-dancing film which includes music from Julian Lennon, Laura Branigan and Roberta Flack?

5 Who had a number one pop hit in 1982 with 'Pass The Dutchie'?

6 Which pop star bought Diana Dors' former home in 1985?

7 'A New England' was a successful recording for which lady?

8 Who directed Michael Jackson's million dollar video *Thriller*?

SOLUTIONS ON PAGE 117

9 Who had their first US gold LP with *Screaming For Vengeance* in 1982?

10 By what name is Yvette Marie Stevens more popularly known?

11 Which pop group of twenty years standing released three anniversary LP's called *Kovers*, *Kollectable* and *Greatest Hits* in 1985?

12 Who made her solo debut in 1982 with 'Something's Going On'?

13 Captain Sensible topped the British Charts in 1982 with a song that had originated from the musical *South Pacific*. What was the title of this song?

14 What was the title of Mick Jagger's first solo single of 1985?

15 With which band do you associate the singer known simply as Green?

SCORE 15 POINTS

THIS AND THAT

1 The duo known as Dollar were originally members of which seventies group?

2 Which Boomtown Rats single was rated Best Single in the British Rock and Pop Awards 1979?

3 'Hot Love' and 'Ride A White Swan' were hit singles of which early seventies group?

4 Jimi Hendrix' first band were known as the Jimi Hendrix Experience. What was the name of his band in 1969?

5 Who is the singer/songwriter who composed Lena Martell's chart topping single 'One Day At A Time' (1979)?

6 Bonnie Tyler became an international success with which hit single of 1978?

SOLUTIONS ON PAGE 117

7 Who wrote 'Every Little Thing She Does Is Magic' (1981)?

8 Soft Cell had only one hit single in 1981, what was it called?

9 Which single from George Harrison's triple album *All Things Must Pass* reached No. one in 1971?

10 Who was the Disc Jockey of the Year from 1960-63?

11 What was the Double A side of Paul McCartney's 'Mull Of Kintyre'?

12 Who left The Faces in 1973 to form his own band Slim Chance?

13 Who was accompanied by birds on her hit single 'Loving You' (1975)?

14 Who had hits in the seventies with 'Keep On Dancing' and 'Remember (Sha-la-la)'?

15 Whose debut album of 1984 was called *Steps In Time*?

16 Which duo sang the title song for the film *Endless Love*?

SOLUTIONS ON PAGE 117

17 Who was the Italian female vocalist who entered the British Top Ten with 'Do It Do It Again' in 1978?

18 Which member of The Beach Boys died in 1983 aged 39?

19 What was the title of The New Seekers hit of 1971 which was a Coca Cola advertisement?

20 Queen and David Bowie teamed up in 1981 and produced a No. one hit single. What was it called?

SCORE 20 POINTS

WHO SANG THAT IN 1985?

Are you able to identify the singer or group who recorded the following songs in 1985?

1 'Won't You Hold My Hand Now?'

2 'Cockney Translation'

3 'Baby U Left Me (In The Cold)'

4 'Walk Like A Man'

5 'That Was Yesterday'

6 'Piece Of The Action'

7 'Cover Me'

8 'Look Mama'

9 'When Love Breaks Down'

10 'I Feel Love'

11 'Wait'

12 'We Are The World'

13 'Eye To Eye'

14 'Don't You (Forget About Me)'

15 'Castles In The Air'

SCORE 15 POINTS

SOLUTIONS ON PAGE 117

Solutions

VIDEO WORDS

1 Bronski Beat
2 'Two Tribes'
3 'Thriller'
4 'Wake Me Up'
5 Limahl
6 'Gimme All Your Lovin''
7 'The War Song'
8 Michael Jackson
9 'Relax'
10 Thomas Dolby
11 Madness
12 'Pride'
13 Nik Kershaw
14 UB40
15 'I'm Still Standing'
16 'The Wild Boys'

You will see that in the highlighted squares is the answer 'Bohemian Rhapsody', which was the first pop promotional video by Queen.

CAN YOU IDENTIFY THE FOLLOWING GROUPS?

1 Duran Duran
2 Bananarama
3 The Monkees
4 Iron Maiden
5 The Commodores
6 Culture Club
7 Spandau Ballet
8 Bucks Fizz
9 Modern Romance
10 Shakatak
11 UB40
12 Police
13 Everything But The Girl
14 Madness
15 A Flock Of Seagulls

SOLO ARTISTS

1 Gary Numan
2 Tracey Ullman
3 Elvis Costello
4 Hazel O'Connor
5 Shakin' Stevens
6 Kim Wilde
7 Michael Jackson
8 Paul Young
9 Howard Jones
10 Madonna
11 Shannon
12 David Sylvian
13 Alison Moyet
14 Alvin Stardust
15 Suzi Quatro

NO. ONE HIT ALBUMS

1 Rod Stewart
2 Fleetwood Mac
3 Roxy Music
4 Lindisfarne
5 Dire Straits
6 Gary Numan
7 Abba
8 Wings
9 Iron Maiden
10 Motorhead
11 Phil Collins
12 Elvis Presley
13 The Faces
14 Kate Bush
15 Genesis

POP FACTS

1 True. Johnny Logan, who is Australian, sang the Irish entry, which became a No. one hit in Britain. It was called 'What's Another Year?'
2 True.
3 False. It was Paul McCartney who received the award from the Guinness Book of World Records.
4 True.
5 False. They originated from Birmingham.
6 False. He earned 37.
7 True.
8 True.
9 True.
10 False. It is Watford Football Club he is associated with.
11 True.
12 False. Buddy Holly was the first person to have a No. one hit after his death. The song was 'It Doesn't Matter Anymore'.
13 False. *The Official BBC Album of the Royal Wedding* did reach No. one in the pop LP charts but stayed there for two weeks in 1981 not 1980.
14 False. It was Frankie Goes To Hollywood's song 'Relax' which was banned by the BBC.
15 False. They are father and daughter.

POP STARS, FILMS AND THEME MUSIC

1 *Watership Down*
2 The Revolution and The Time
3 *Alice's Restaurant*
4 Ned Kelly
5 St Matthew
6 Billie Holliday
7 Buffy Sainte-Marie

8 George Harrison
9 'Free Me', sung by Roger Daltrey
10 *Breaking Glass*
11 Eurythmics

12 Ray Parker Jr
13 Tina Turner
14 Irene Cara
15 Prince

ALSO KNOWN AS . . .

1 Alice Cooper
2 Adam Ant
3 Little Richard
4 Smokey Robinson
5 Cher (of Sonny And Cher)
6 P. J. Proby
7 Cliff Richard
8 Donna Summer

9 Frankie Avalon
10 Prince
11 Elvis Costello
12 Connie Francis
13 Marc Bolan
14 Gary Numan
15 Boy George

ALL SORTS

1 Stiff Little Fingers
2 Kajagoogoo
3 Winston
4 Wizzard
5 Dustman
6 Nick Rhodes
7 'Albatross'
8 Sex Pistols

9 David Sylvian
10 Paul Gambaccini
11 Michael Jackson
12 Grace Jones
13 Status Quo
14 Wham!
15 Sting

POP DUOS

1 Julio Iglesias and Diana Ross
2 Diana Ross and Lionel Richie
3 Jan and Dean
4 B A Robertson and Maggie Bell
5 Zager and Evans
6 John Travolta and Olivia Newton John
7 Dave Stewart and Barbara Gaskin
8 Frank and Nancy Sinatra
9 Sonny and Cher
10 Daryl Hall and John Oates
11 Chas and Dave
12 Paul McCartney and the Frog Chorus

13 Barbra Streisand and Neil Diamond
14 Johnny Mathis and Deniece Williams
15 Carly Simon and James Taylor

ELVIS

1 East Tupelo, Mississippi
2 Gladys
3 'All Shook Up'
4 The Dorsey Brothers
5 *Love Me Tender*
6 Graceland
7 *King Creole*
8 Priscilla Beaulieu
9 Lisa Marie
10 1977 (16 August)
11 Aron
12 'Jailhouse Rock'
13 *GI Blues*
14 'Can't Help Falling In Love'
15 'Way Down'

GOLDEN OLDIES

1 'I Believe' (1953)
2 'Rock Around The Clock' (1955)
3 'Three Steps To Heaven' (1960)
4 'Tell Laura I Love Her' (1960)
5 'That'll Be The Day' (1957)
6 'Moon River' (1961)
7 'Why Do Fools Fall In Love?' (1956)
8 'You'll Never Walk Alone' (1963)
9 'Jailhouse Rock' (1958)
10 'Shakin' All Over' (1960)

INSTRUMENTS

1 Mike Oldfield
2 Paul McCartney
3 Andy Taylor
4 Sitar
5 Stewart Copeland
6 Jimi Hendrix
7 Drums (The Honeycombs were one of the first rock groups to have a female drummer).
8 Trumpet
9 Ian Anderson
10 Elton John. Piano

IN COMMON

1 They were all Elvis Presley's managers.
2 All punk rock bands.

3 They were titles of instrumental records. 'Apache' by The Shadows, 'Roulette' by Russ Conway and 'Rebel Rouser' by Duane Eddy.

4 They were the original four members of Led Zeppelin.

5 All Abba albums.

6 All songs from films which reached No. one. 'Secret Love' was from *Calamity Jane* and sung by Doris Day (1954). Cliff Richard sang 'Summer Holiday' (1963) in the film of the same name. 'You're The One That I Want' (1978) sung by John Travolta and Olivia Newton John was from the film *Grease*.

7 They have all sung duets with Barbra Streisand. Barbra Streisand and Barry Gibb recorded 'Guilty' in 1980. Barbra Streisand and Neil Diamond recorded 'You Don't Bring Me Flowers' in 1978. Barbra Streisand and Donna Summer recorded 'No More Tears (Enough Is Enough)' (1979).

8 The names of these groups give the impression that each member is related. This is not the case in any of these groups.

9 All are blind performers. Lenny Peters was the other half of the duo Peters and Lee.

10 They all sang the theme tunes of James Bond movies. Shirley Bassey sang 'Diamonds Are Forever', Paul McCartney sang 'Live And Let Die' and Carly Simon, 'Nobody Does It Better' from *The Spy Who Loved Me*.

TRUE OR FALSE?

1 True.

2 False. He was with the Commodores.

3 True.

4 True.

5 False. This is the title of the official biography of Culture Club.

6 False. Divine is a man. One of his 'real' names is Glenn Muldoon.

7 False. It was a Michael Jackson and Paul McCartney duet on the *Thriller* album.

8 False. They are all from *The Serious Moonlight Tour*, an album recorded live at the Pacific National Coliseum, Vancouver, Canada.

9 False. They presented *The Tube*.

10 False. It was the debut album of Nik Kershaw.

POP STARS AND FILMS

1 The Beatles
2 Cliff Richard
3 Pete Townsend
4 Elvis Presley
5 John Travolta
6 The Dave Clark Five
7 Barbra Streisand and
  Kris Kristofferson
8 Johnny Rotten
9 Bob Dylan
10 David Bowie
11 Bob Geldof
12 Neil Diamond
13 Diana Ross
14 Michael Jackson
  (and Diana Ross)
15 Olivia Newton John

VIDEO, VIDEO

1 The Cars
2 Duran Duran
3 Spandau Ballet
4 Paul Young
5 Motorhead
6 Bronski Beat
7 Adam Ant
8 David Bowie
9 Eurythmics
10 Culture Club

☆ ☆ ☆ ☆ ☆ BONUS TIME ☆ ☆ ☆ ☆ ☆

1 'The Times They Are
  A-Changin''
  'Subterranean Homesick
  Blues'
  'Like A Rolling Stone'
  'Positively Fourth Street'
2 1970
3 'The Minute You're Gone'
  1965
4 'Charmaine' 1963
  'Diane' 1964
  'Ramona' 1964

  'Marie' 1965
  'Hello Dolly' 1966
  'Marta' 1967
5 'Shaddup Your Face'
6 Columbia
  Decca
  HMV
  Pye
7 Dennis Waterman
8 Culture Club
9 'So Near To Christmas'
10 Robert Plant

THE BEATLES AND AFTER

1 **d** George Harrison, born 25 February 1943. (John, October 1940;
  Paul, June 1942; Ringo, July 1940.)
2 **b** Pete Best. Ringo Starr replaced him in 1962.
3 **c** The Cavern.
4 **c** 1963.
5 **d** *Please Please Me* was released in 1963, followed by *With The*

Beatles. A Hard Day's Night followed in 1964. All three albums topped the British Album Charts.

6 c *A Hard Day's Night.*
7 a John Lennon.
8 b 1966.
9 b Apple. They also had an Apple clothes boutique.
10 d *The White Album.*
11 c George Harrison.
12 b *Live And Let Die.*
13 c *Double Fantasy.*
14 c The Rebels. It was John Lennon who formed The Quarrymen in 1955. The Quarrymen later became the Silver Beatles and then The Beatles.
15 c George Harrison.
16 a He loved wearing lots of rings.
17 d Candy. He played a Mexican gardener.
18 c Michael Jackson.
19 c 1980.
20 d Sean. Julian (born 1964) was his son by his first marriage to Cynthia. Sean was born in October 1975.

LEAD SINGERS AND THEIR GROUPS

1 Siouxsie And The Banshees
2 Ian Dury And The Blockheads
3 Echo And The Bunnymen
4 Geno Washington And The Ram Jam Band
5 Elvis Costello And The Attractions
6 Bob Marley And The Wailers
7 Father Abraham And The Smurfs
8 Kid Creole And The Coconuts
9 Mamas And The Papas
10 Sly And The Family Stone

POP STARS AND FILMS 2

1 Duran Duran
2 Paul McCartney
3 Pink Floyd
4 *American Gigolo*
5 *The Bears And I*
6 Queen
7 Sting (from Police)
8 Alan Price
9 *Electric Dreams*
10 Randy Newman

SINGING THE BLUES

1 Elvis Presley
2 The Goons
3 Chelsea Football Club
4 Cliff Richard
5 Fats Domino
6 Eddie Cochran
7 Rolf Harris
8 Linda Ronstadt
9 David Bowie
10 Roy Orbison

COMPLETE THE TITLES

1 'Love's Great Adventure'
2 'I'm Gonna Tear Your Playhouse Down'
3 'All Cried Out'
4 'Do They Know It's Cristmas?'
5 'Hotline To Heaven'
6 'The Never Ending Story'
7 'Too Late For Goodbyes'
8 'Do The Conga'
9 'I'm So Beautiful'
10 'Listen To Your Father'
11 'All Through The Night'
12 'Back In My Arms'
13 'We Are Family'
14 'Never Turn Away'
15 'The Power Of Love'

THREE TIMES A LADY

1 Human League
2 The Four Tops
3 Little Richard
4 Barry Ryan
5 Slim Whitman
6 The Bluebells
7 Cliff Richard
8 Malcolm McLaren
9 Buddy Holly
10 Barry Manilow
11 Scott Walker
12 Police
13 John Travolta
14 The Hollies
15 Simon And Garfunkel

SKELETON QUIZ

1 Strawberry Switchblade
2 Liz Fraser
3 Sarah Brightman
4 Pat Benatar
5 Kate St John
6 Amii Stewart
7 Bananarama
8 Tracey Thorn
9 Barbara Dickson
10 Kirsty McColl
11 Alison Moyet
12 June Miles Kingston
13 Gill Saward
14 Kim Carnes
15 Tina Turner
16 Chaka Khan
17 Alannah Currie
18 Cheryl Baker
19 Lulu
20 Madonna
21 Joan Armatrading
22 Helen Terry

ROCK IN THE EIGHTIES

1 Frankie Goes To Hollywood
2 Tin Tin
3 Richard Drummie and
   Peter Cox
4 *Body Rock*
5 Musical Youth
6 George Michael (of Wham!)
7 Kirsty MacColl
8 John Landis
9 Judas Priest
10 Chaka Khan
11 The Kinks
12 Frida (of Abba)
13 'Happy Talk'
14 'Just Another Night'
15 Scritti Politti

THIS AND THAT

1 Guys And Dolls
2 'I Don't Like Mondays'
3 T Rex
4 The Band Of Gypsies
5 Kris Kristofferson
6 'It's A Heartache'
7 Sting
8 'Tainted Love'
9 'My Sweet Lord'
10 David Jacobs
11 'Girl's School'
12 Ronnie Laine
13 Minnie Riperton
14 Bay City Rollers
15 King
16 Lionel Richie and Diana Ross
17 Raffaella Carra
18 Dennis Wilson
19 'I'd Like To Teach The World
   To Sing'
20 'Under Pressure'

WHO SANG THAT IN 1985?

1 King
2 Smiley Culture
3 Marilyn
4 Divine
5 Foreigner
6 Meat Loaf
7 Bruce Springsteen
8 Howard Jones
9 Prefab Sprout
10 Bronski Beat with
   Marc Almond
11 The Jacksons
12 USA For Africa
13 Chaka Khan
14 Simple Minds
15 The Colour Field

How well did you do?

*Maximum score 382. If you scored
more than 150 – that's cool; more than
200 – fast mover; over 250 – top of the
chart.*

Films

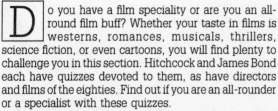

D o you have a film speciality or are you an all-round film buff? Whether your taste in films is westerns, romances, musicals, thrillers, science fiction, or even cartoons, you will find plenty to challenge you in this section. Hitchcock and James Bond each have quizzes devoted to them, as have directors and films of the eighties. Find out if you are an all-rounder or a specialist with these quizzes.

How well do you know your film stars, their range of films and backgrounds? Can you identify the stars from their real names? A few of the answers may surprise you. Some films are based on true life stories, can you identify the subjects of these films? Play film Bingo, identify the Disney songs, find the deliberate mistakes and collect extra points with the bonus questions. These quizzes will keep you guessing for some time.

A QUESTION OF LISTS

In each of the following questions there are a number of answers which are required. We give you one answer, can you complete the remainder?

1 James Dean only made three major films, two of which were released posthumously. Can you name these films?

_____ _____ _____   (1955)

_____ _____ _____ _____   (1956)

Giant   (1956)

2 Are you able to name the three men that Marilyn Monroe married?

1942   Jim Dougherty

1954   _____ _____ _____

1956   _____ _____

3 Which male actors starred opposite Glenda Jackson in the following films?

Sunday Bloody Sunday (1971)   Murray Head

A Touch Of Class (1972)   _____ _____

Bequest To The Nation (1973)   _____ _____

House Calls (1978)   _____ _____

4 Who were the husband-and-wife teams that were involved in the following films?

Who's Afraid Of
Virginia Woolf? (1966)   Elizabeth Taylor and Richard Burton

To Be Or Not To Be
(1983)   _____ _____ _____ _____ _____

Harry And Son (1984)   _____ _____ _____ _____ _____

5 Can you identify the John Travolta film from the following roles?

Tony Manero   Saturday Night Fever (1977)

Danny Zuko   _____ (1978)

Bud Davis   _____ _____ (1980)

6 Bing Crosby, Dorothy Lamour and Bob Hope made six Road films, can you identify them?

Road to Singapore	(1940)	Road to _____	(1945)
Road to _____	(1941)	Road to _____	(1947)
Road to _____	(1942)	Road to _____	(1952)

SOLUTIONS ON PAGE 161

7 The Marx Brothers all chose their own inimitable stage names. Can you identify them from their real names?

Julius Henry	Groucho
Adolph Arthur	
Leonard	
Herbert	

8 Can you identify the authors who created the following 'Doctors' who became screen characters?

Dr Jekyll	Robert Louis Stevenson
Dr Zhivago	_____ _____
Dr Dolittle	_____ _____
Dr Faustus	_____ _____
Doctor In The House	_____ _____

9 Some of Charles Dickens' novels have been adapted for musical films. Can you identify the novels upon which the following films were based?

Oliver! (1968)	Oliver Twist
Scrooge (1970)	_____ _____ _____
Mr Quilp (1975)	_____ _____ _____ _____

SOLUTIONS ON PAGE 161

10 Who played the anti-heroes in the following films?

From Here To Eternity
(1953)   Montgomery Clift
The Wild One (1954)   _____ _____
Saturday Night And
Sunday Morning (1960)   _____ _____

SCORE 10 POINTS

FILM THEMES

Are you able to identify the themes of the following films from the list given?

1 Kramer v Kramer (1979)
2 Harry And Tonto (1974)
3 Willard (1971)
4 Papillon (1973)
5 A Day In The Death Of Joe Egg (1971)
6 Barry Lyndon (1975)
7 Norma Rae (1979)
8 The China Syndrome (1979)
9 Reds (1981)
10 Raiders Of The Lost Ark (1981)

A A young man trains rats to kill his enemies.

SOLUTIONS ON PAGE 161

B Parents frustrated by difficulties with their disabled daughter.
C Unionization in a southern American factory.
D Separation, divorce and child custody.
E The dangers of nuclear power.
F Autobiography of life on Devil's Island.
G American archaeologist beats Nazis in finding a priceless item.
H John Reed's story of revolution and the formation of the American Communist Party.
I The adventures of an 18th-century Irish gentleman.
J A New York widower and his cat trek to Chicago.

SCORE 10 POINTS

SPORTING FILMS

Can you identify the sport that featured in the following films?

1	*The Baltimore Bullet* (1980)	**6**	*Chariots Of Fire* (1981)
2	*The Champ* (1979)	**7**	*Semi-Tough* (1977)
3	*Champions* (1984)	**8**	*Bobby Deerfield* (1977)
4	*Breaking Away* (1979)	**9**	*Players* (1979)
5	*Slap Shot* (1977)	**10**	*The Bad News Bears* (1976)

SCORE 10 POINTS

SOLUTIONS ON PAGE 162

BONUS QUESTIONS

1 Which star actress played the blind young wife who was terrorized by narcotics smugglers in the 1967 film *Wait Until Dark*?

2 Which American actress starred in the 1984 film of John Le Carré's novel *The Little Drummer Girl*?

3 Who played the title roles in the film *Dirty Mary, Crazy Larry* (1974)?

4 Which male sex-symbol played an American Jewish gambler opposite Barbra Streisand in *Funny Girl* (1968)?

5 What was the title of Steve McQueen's final film of 1980, when he played Ralph 'Papa' Thorson?

6 Which popular film of 1963 had the secondary title ... *Or How I Learned To Stop Worrying And Love The Bomb*?

7 Which actor played all eight victims in the Ealing comedy *Kind Hearts And Coronets* (1949)?

8 Which huge English actor made his film debut at the age of sixty, playing the fat man in *The Maltese Falcon* (1931)?

9 Which British actress was cast as Juliet in the 1968 film *Romeo And Juliet*?

10 Which actress's life story was told in *Mommie Dearest* (1983)?

11 Which pop star played Baron Frankenstein in *The Bride* (1984)?

12 Who wrote *Bring On The Empty Horses*, a book of random collections of Hollywood and its leading lights?

SOLUTIONS ON PAGE 163

★ **13** Who was the male star of *Reuben, Reuben* (1984)?

★ **14** Which actress was married to Peter Sellers from 1963-68?

★ **15** Which actress do you associate with the films *Paper Moon* (1973) and *Nickelodeon* (1978)?

SCORE 2 POINTS FOR EACH CORRECT ANSWER

★★★★★★★★★★★★★★★★★★★★★★★★★★★★★★★★★★★★

OSCARS

Can you complete the sentences by filling in the blanks?

1 _____ _____ won an Oscar for Best Actress for her portrayal of Aurora in *Terms Of Endearment* (1984).

2 An Oscar was awarded for _____ _____ _____, the Best Original Song in *Flashdance* (1984).

3 _____ _____ was given an Oscar for her first starring role in a film. The film was *Roman Holiday* (1953).

4 _____ _____ was nominated for Oscars for *They Shoot Horses Don't They?* (1969), *Julia* (1977), *The China Syndrome* (1979) and *On Golden Pond* (1981). She won Oscars in _____ (1971) and _____ _____ (1978).

5 _____ _____ won the Best Actress Oscar in 1980 for her performance in *Coalminer's Daughter*.

6 Yul Brynner won an Oscar for Best Actor, playing the proud and supercilious King of Siam in _____ _____ _____ _____ (1956).

7 _____ _____ _____ won notoriety as the first actor to refuse to accept an Oscar. He had been nominated for his role in _____.

8 _____ _____ was nominated for several Oscars and was awarded three: for her performances in *Gaslight* (1944), *Anastasia* (1956) and *Murder On The Orient Express* (1974).

SOLUTIONS ON PAGE 163

9 Peter Finch was awarded the first posthumous Oscar for his role in _____ (1976).

10 _____ _____ won an Oscar for her portrayal of Scarlet O'Hara in _Gone With The Wind_ (1939).

SCORE 10 POINTS

FAMOUS FILM ACTORS – AND THEIR TELEVISION ROLES

Can you identify the following famous film actors who have also appeared in popular television series?

1 He played Rodney Harrington, the 'decent and honest' young man in the American soap opera _Peyton Place_ and starred in _What's Up Doc_ (1972). Who am I describing?

2 He was nominated for an Oscar for _Birdman Of Alcatraz_ (1961) and achieved sensational fame on television as a lollipop sucking New York cop. Who am I describing?

3 This American star played the title role in _Jennie_, a television series concerning the Churchills, and the adoptive mother of a demonic child in _The Omen_ (1976). Who am I describing?

4 She died of leukemia in the tear-jerking film _Love Story_ (1970) and starred opposite Robert Mitchum in the television epic _The Winds Of War_. Who am I describing?

5 This actress won Oscars for _Women In Love_ (1969) and _A Touch Of Class_ (1972), and also played the title role in the television series _Elizabeth R_. Who am I describing?

6 He played private eye _Marlowe_ (1969) in the Raymond Chandler film adaptation and is known for a similar role in television's _The Rockford Files_. Who am I describing?

7 He directed himself in the title role of _The Outlaw Josey Wales_ (1976) and played Rowdy Yates in the television series _Rawhide_. Who am I describing?

8 This actress initially made her reputation in the television serial

SOLUTIONS ON PAGE 163

A For Andromeda in 1962 and later starred as Lara in *Doctor Zhivago* (1965). Who am I describing?

9 Ronald Reagan was one of the four ex-husbands of this actress, who won an Oscar in *Johnny Belinda* (1948). Her role as the matriarch of *Falcon Crest* brought her television recognition. Who am I describing?

10 The musical star of *Kiss Me Kate* (1953), *Seven Brides For Seven Brothers* (1954) and *Calamity Jane* (1953) became a television star in the popular soap opera *Dallas*. Who am I describing?

SCORE 10 POINTS

HORROR

Can you complete the titles of the following horror films?

1 *An American* _____ _____ _____ (1981)
2 _____ _____ *Rides Out* (1967)
3 *The Texas* _____ _____ (1974)
4 _____ *Baby* (1968)
5 *The Postman* _____ _____ _____ (1981)

SOLUTIONS ON PAGE 163

6 *Dr* _____ *And Mr* _____ (1941)
7 _____ *II: The Possession* (1982)
8 *Whatever Happened To* _____ _____ (1962)
9 *Dressed* _____ _____ (1980)
10 *The* _____ *Staircase* (1975)

SCORE 10 POINTS

SCIENCE FICTION

How well do you know the following films?

1 *2001: A Space Odyssey* was based on a story by Arthur C. Clarke. What was the original title of this story?

2 In which Steven Spielberg film of 1982 is the five-year-old Carol Anne kidnapped when ghosts fly out of the television set?

3 Who played Roy Neary, the electrical worker who experiences a strange phenomenon while driving his truck one night in *Close Encounters Of The Third Kind* (1977)?

4 Can you name any one of the actors who starred in the 1968 film *Planet Of The Apes*?

SOLUTIONS ON PAGE 164

5 What is the name of the young boy who befriends E.T., the Extra-Terrestrial when he is accidentally left on Earth?

6 What was the title of the sequel to *Raiders Of The Lost Ark* (1981)?

7 Name the two robots which appear in all the *Star Wars* films?

8 Who was nominated for an Academy Award for his music in *Superman* (1978)?

9 What was the subtitle of the *Star Trek II* movie of 1982?

10 Who wrote and directed *A Clockwork Orange* (1971), a film adaptation of Anthony Burgess's novel?

SCORE 10 POINTS

SONGS IN FILMS

Name the film you would associate with the following songs.

1 'Evergreen'

2 'Ding Dong! The Witch Is Dead'

3 'Count Your Blessings'

4 'Supercalifragilisticexpialidocious'

5 'When Doves Cry'

6 'If You Could See Her With My Eyes'

7 'You're The One That I Want'

8 'Sold My Soul To Rock'n'Roll'

9 'In The Name Of Love'

10 'March Of The Siamese Children'

SOLUTIONS ON PAGE 164

11 'Wand'rin Star'

12 'Moon River'

13 'Mrs Robinson'

14 'I Could Have Danced All Night'

15 'Maria'

SCORE 15 POINTS

JAMES BOND

Are you a Bond addict? Fill in the correct answers for the following.

1 _____ _____ played Bond's Secret Service boss until his death.

2 The stories for most of the James Bond films are based on novels by _____ _____.

3 The seductive song 'Nobody Does It Better' was the theme song from _____ _____ _____ _____ _____ (1977). It was sung by _____ _____.

SOLUTIONS ON PAGE 164

4 _____ _____ was the first James Bond adventure movie, in 1962.

5 The villainous servant _____ had a razor-sharp bowler hat in *Goldfinger* (1964).

6 Sean Connery returned to the Bond role for the 1984 film _____ _____ _____ _____.

7 _____ is 007's boss.

8 _____ was known as 'the man with the Midas touch'.

9 _____ is Bond's gadget maker.

10 'The Look Of Love' was the popular song from the James Bond spoof movie, _____ _____ (1967).

11 Lois Maxwell played the frustrated _____ _____, M's secretary.

12 *You Only Live Twice* was set in _____.

SOLUTIONS ON PAGE 164

13 SPECTRE is the enemy organization in many of the Bond films. The initials represent ＿＿＿ ＿＿＿ ＿＿＿ ＿＿＿ ＿＿＿ ＿＿＿ ＿＿＿.

14 ＿＿＿ ＿＿＿ played Bond in *On Her Majesty's Secret Service* (1969).

15 ＿＿＿ ＿＿＿ abandoned his Dracula roles to play the villainous Scaramanga in *The Man With The Golden Gun*.

16 Roger Moore first played James Bond in ＿＿＿ ＿＿＿ ＿＿＿ ＿＿＿.

17 ＿＿＿ (1979) was Ian Fleming's last available novel for the Bond treatment.

18 Richard Kiel was the 7 foot 2 inch actor who played the cobalt-steel-toothed killer called ＿＿＿.

19 ＿＿＿ ＿＿＿ ＿＿＿ ＿＿＿ was the first Bond film in which Ian Fleming did not gain a credit.

20 ＿＿＿ ＿＿＿ was the first actor to portray SPECTRE chief Ernst Stavro Blofeld, in *You Only Live Twice* (1967).

SCORE 20 POINTS

IN COMMON

Can you identify one thing that each of the following groups has in common?

1 *The Lost Weekend* (1945) and *Days Of Wine And Roses* (1962)

2 Racquel Welch, Julie Andrews and Mia Farrow

3 *Morning Glory* (1933), *Guess Who's Coming To Dinner* (1967) and *The Lion In Winter* (1968)

4 *Nashville* (1975), *Three Women* (1977) and *Come Back To The Five-and-Dime, Jimmy Dean, Jimmy Dean* (1982)

SOLUTIONS ON PAGE 165

5 *Born Free* (1966), *Romeo And Juliet* (1968) and *West Side Story* (1962)

6 *Lust For Life* (1956), *The Moon And Sixpence* (1943) and *The Agony And The Ecstacy* (1965)

7 *The Alamo* (1960), *The Cowboys* (1972) and *The Shootist* (1976)

8 *The House Of Fear* (1945), *The Hound Of The Baskervilles* (1939) and *The Scarlet Claw* (1944)

9 *Alice Doesn't Live Here Anymore* (1974), *A Star Is Born* (1976) and *Pat Garrett And Billy The Kid* (1973)

10 *Klute* (1971), *Easy Rider* (1969) and *On Golden Pond* (1981)

11 *The Blue Lagoon* (1980), *The Adventures Of Robinson Crusoe* (1938) and *The Admirable Crichton* (1957)

12 *Blazing Saddles* (1974), *Silent Movie* (1976) and *History Of The World Part One* (1981)

13 Marni Nixon, *My Fair Lady* (1964) and *West Side Story* (1961)

14 Lewis Wilson, Adam West and Robert Lowery

15 Sir Michael Redgrave, Ramon Navarro and George C. Scott

SCORE 15 POINTS

FILM CHARACTERS
Unscramble the letters to reveal the film in which the following characters appeared.

1 Daddy Warbucks (1982)   NANIE
2 Aurora Greenway (1984)   MEET SOFT MEN NEAR RD
3 Caractacus Potts (1968) BYBY TITCHNAG TITCHNAG
4 Jack Terry (1983)   WOOL BUT
5 Fast Eddie Felson (1961) STRUTH HEEL
6 Selina (1984)   RULER PIGS

SOLUTIONS ON PAGE 165

7 Popeye Doyle (1971)   CHIC CHEET FENNROOTNN
8 Mrs Robinson (1967)   DARTH GAUTEE
9 Esther Hoffman Howard   A RATS ROBINS
(1976)
10 Mr Bunnies and Mr   JR OF MOCANTODY
McCools (1984)

SCORE 10 POINTS

WHO SAID THAT ...?

Can you identify the actor with the following lines?

1 'You ain't heard nothin' yet, folks.'

2 'Love means never having to say you're sorry ...'

3 'What's up Doc'?'

4 'Here's looking at you, kid.'

5 'You dirty rat.'

SOLUTIONS ON PAGE 166

6 'Frankly my dear, I don't give a damn.'

7 'I want to be alone ...'

8 'The rain in Spain stays mainly in the plain ...'

9 'Nobody who hates children and small dogs can be all bad.'

10 'I coulda had class! I coulda been a contender! I coulda been somebody! Instead of a bum, which is what I am!'

SCORE 10 POINTS

STAGE NAMES

Film stars often change their names to fit their screen persona. Can you identify the following film stars from their real names?

1 Julia Elizabeth Wells
2 Richard Jenkins
3 Bernard Schwartz
4 Doris Kappelhoff
5 Sophia Scicolone

6 Norma Jean Baker
7 Harold Webb
8 Shirley Schrift
9 Marion Michael Morrison
10 Virginia McMath

SCORE 10 POINTS

A MIXED BAG

1 What was the title of the Chubby Checker film which holds the world record as the film made in the shortest time – 28 days?

2 Which film actor and director left the United States after the Second World War to live in Switzerland because of his supposed Communist sympathies?

3 What did *The Last Picture Show* (1971), *The Exorcist* (1973), *Same Time Next Year* (1978) and *Resurrection* (1980) have in common?

4 In film jargon, what is the word used to describe the hinged board on which details of each shot are recorded?

SOLUTIONS ON PAGE 166

5 With which film do you associate the songs 'Dance at the Gym Tonight' and 'I Have a Love'?

6 What was the title of the film from the William Golding novel of the same name which told the story of a plane load of evacuee boys who were marooned on a desert island?

7 What was the name of the family who were portrayed in the film *The Sound Of Music* (1965)?

8 Who was the first film star in the US to be honoured with the issue of a postage stamp bearing his picture?

9 Douglas Bader, the great RAF hero, was immortalised on film. What was the title of the film which told his life story?

10 Who was the leading bandleader of the swing era who married Lana Turner (his second wife) and Ava Gardner (his fourth wife)?

SCORE 10 POINTS

SOLUTIONS ON PAGE 166

CHARACTER TYPES

Can you match the following character types with the list of actors? there are a few red herrings here too.

1	Ice maiden	Christopher Lee
2	Macho tough guy	Robert Redford
3	King of British horror	Alain Delon
4	International heart-throb	Albert Finney
5	Dance king	John Travolta
6	The modern American urban man	Burt Reynolds
		Steve McQueen
7	The modern Chaplin	Omar Sharif
8	The Sundance Kid	George Segal
9	Working-class hero	Ursula Andress
10	French gangster	Brigitte Bardot
		Woody Allen
		Charles Bronson

SCORE 10 POINTS

GREAT MALE LOVERS OF THE SCREEN

Find the heart-throb in the film. The initials of the star are provided for the impatient.

1	*Carrie* (1976)	JT
2	*Son Of The Sheik* (1926)	RV
3	*Where Eagles Dare* (1969)	CE
4	*Barefoot In The Park* (1967)	RR
5	*The Cincinnati Kid* (1968)	SM
6	*On The Waterfront* (1954)	MB
7	*Pillow Talk* (1959)	RH
8	*Death Race 2000* (1975)	SS
9	*New York, New York* (1977)	RDN
10	*Diamonds Are Forever* (1971)	SC
11	*Hud* (1963)	PN
12	*Love Story* (1970)	RO
13	*A Star Is Born* (1976)	KK
14	*The Graduate* (1968)	DH
15	*Starting Over* (1979)	BR

SCORE 15 POINTS

SOLUTIONS ON PAGE 166

DISNEY SONGS

Disney's films are made even more memorable by the number of popular songs contained within them. Are you able to identify the Disney films from the following songs?

1 'Bibbidy-Bobbidy-Boo'
2 'Feed The Birds'
3 'Whistle While You Work'
4 'When You Wish Upon A Star'
5 'Who's Afraid Of The Big Bad Wolf?'
6 'The Bare Necessities'
7 'Love Is A Song'
8 'He's A Tramp'
9 'He Danced With Me'
10 'Zip-a-dee-doo-dah'

SCORE 10 POINTS

WHAT A LAUGH!

Can you answer the following questions concerning film comedies and their stars?

1 The films *The Bank* (1916), *The Cure* (1917) and *The Gold Rush* (1925) all starred which early film comedian?

2 Who was the comedian of the twenties known for his famous spine-chilling 'human fly' stunt in *Safety Last* (1923)?

3 Which child-hating comedian was the star of *Never Give A Sucker An Even Break* (1941)?

4 Who played a Georgia bootlegger who was chased by a petty, stupid, fat sheriff in the chase comedy *Smokey And The Bandit* (1977)?

5 Joe E. Brown starred in which mad Stanley Kramer comedy of 1963?

6 Who wrote and starred in the sixties comedy *What's New Pussycat* (1965)?

7 Who played Chauncey Gardiner, the man whose only knowledge of life was based on television viewing, in the ironic comedy film *Being There* (1979)?

SOLUTIONS ON PAGE 167

8 Who played the screen lovers in the romantic comedy *Pillow Talk* (1959)?

9 In which sharp comedy directed by John Landis in 1983 did Dan Ackroyd play a well-bred white man who changed places in society with a low-life black hustler, with hilarious consequences?

10 Which Disney production of 1983 revolved around the love affair of a mermaid and a vegetable wholesaler?

SCORE 10 POINTS

HITCHCOCK – THE MASTER OF SUSPENSE
Hitchcock is known as the master of suspense. How well do you know his films?

1 Richard Hannay was the hero of this spy-thriller (1935) based on a novel by John Buchan. Peggy Ashcroft also starred in the film. The film was:

a *Greenmantle*   **c** *Mr Standfast*
b *The Three Hostages*   **d** *The Thirty-nine Steps*

SOLUTIONS ON PAGE 167

2 His first 'talkie' film (1929) includes a spectacular chase in the British Museum where the 'baddie' falls to his death through the domed roof of the Reading Room. Which film is it?
a *The Manxman*
b *Blackmail*
c *The Lodger*
d *Downhill*

3 Charles Laughton played Sir Humphrey Penhaligon, the wicked squire in Hitchcock's adaptation (1939) of a novel by Daphne du Maurier. What was the title of this film?
a *Rebecca*
b *Jamaica Inn*
c *The Loving Spirit*
d *The House On The Strand*

4 Who was cast as Maxim de Winter, the lord and master of Manderley in Hitchcock's *Rebecca* (1940)? Was it:
a George Sanders
b David Niven
c Nigel Bruce
d Laurence Olivier

SOLUTIONS ON PAGE 168

5 A retired tennis champion plans to murder his wealthy wife, but his plan goes wrong. Which film (1954) was this?
  a *Dial M For Murder*
  b *Rear Window*
  c *I Confess*
  d *Stage Fright*

6 Cary Grant and Grace Kelly were the stars of this Hitchcock film of 1955, which was billed as a comedy-mystery. One memorable chase takes place in a flower market. The film was:
  a *Rear Window*
  b *To Catch A Thief*
  c *The Birds*
  d *Strangers On A Train*

7 Which Hitchcock film (1958), set in San Francisco relied on the basic, universal fear of falling? Was it:
  a *The Man Who Knew Too Much*
  b *The Wrong Man*
  c *Torn Curtain*
  d *Vertigo*

8 One of the most famous sequences from this film (1959) showed Cary Grant being tracked and trapped by a crop-spraying plane. Which film was it?
  a *The Trouble With Harry*
  b *The Paradine Case*
  c *North By Northwest*
  d *Under Capricorn*

9 Janet Leigh, a major star, disappears early in this sixties Hitchcock thriller (1960) when she is stabbed to death in the shower. What was the name of the motel owner who killed her?
  a Tony Perkins   **c** Norman Perkins
  b Morris Bateman   **d** Norman Bates

10 Julie Andrews and Paul Newman were the stars in which Hitchcock thriller (1966), set partially in East Germany?
  a *Frenzy*   **c** *Topaz*
  b *Torn Curtain*   **d** *Marnie*

SCORE 10 POINTS

SOLUTIONS ON PAGE 168

BINGO

Complete a line, then try for a full house!! Using the list of clues, can you enlarge on the initials given?

	1 B	2 RC	3 FL	4 KD	5 AWWYC
6 S		7 TAQ	8 DN	9 TDP	10 ZZG
11 ML	12 M		13 DH	14 OGP	15 DJAMH
16 BD	17 D	18 JV		19 SP	20 RC
21 MB	22 OMR	23 MP	24 C		25 JS
26 Q	27 MC	28 TSVDM	29 OS	30 CL	

BINGO CLUES

1 Rocky's surname.
2 John Wayne's 1975 title role as the old one-eyed US Marshall who teamed up with a tough missionary's daughter.
3 The name of the exorcist in *The Exorcist* (1973).
4 He played the title role in *Spartacus* (1960).
5 The sequel to *Every Which Way But Loose* (1978).
6 A 1979 film concerning life in borstal.
7 C. S. Forester's novel turned into a popular fifties film starring Humphrey Bogart and Katharine Hepburn.

SOLUTIONS ON PAGE 168

8 He played the title role in *Paper Tiger* (1975).

9 The name of the newspaper *Superman* (1978) worked on.

10 The former 'Miss Hungary' who became a film star.

11 American operatic tenor who played his idol, Caruso, in films.

12 The name of the underground creatures in *The Time Machine* (1960).

13 Actor who played 'Dorothy' in *Tootsie* (1982).

14 Henry Fonda's final film.

15 The first-ever horror film, released in 1908.

16 A sex symbol of the eighties.

17 The name of the spacecraft in *2001: A Space Odyssey* (1968).

18 The author of *Around The World In Eighty Days* (1956).

19 Musical adapted from James Michener's Pulitzer Prize winning novel.

20 He played Louis XIV of France in the TV film *The Man In The Iron Mask* (1976).

21 His first feature-length film was *The Producers* (1967).

22 Paul Robeson became famous for his rendition of this song.

23 Mr Dawes was the president of the bank in this musical.

24 Sinatra's 'My Kind of Town' from the musical *Robin And The Seven Hoods* (1964).

25 He played the title role in *The Glenn Miller Story* (1954).

26 Esmeralda befriended this deformed man.

27 The stagename of Maurice Micklewhite.

28 The 1967 film of twenties gang warfare between Al Capone and Bugs Moran.

29 The sequel to *Love Story* (1970).

30 British actor who gained fame with his portrayal of Dracula.

SCORE 30 POINTS

TRUE LIFE STORIES

Can you identify the real-life person whose life story was told in the following films?

1 *Brother Sun, Sister Moon* (1973)
2 *The Music Lovers* (1970)
3 *The Elephant Man* (1980)
4 *The Spirit Of St Louis* (1957)
5 *Running Brave* (1984)
6 *A Song Of Summer* (1984)

SOLUTIONS ON PAGE 168

7 *A Man For All Seasons* (1966)
8 *The Miracle Worker* (1962)
9 *Ten Rillington Place* (1970)
10 *The Inn Of The Sixth Happiness* (1958)
11 *Annie Get Your Gun* (1950)
12 *Funny Girl* (1968)
13 *Lady Sings The Blues* (1972)
14 *Stevie* (1978)
15 *The Incredible Sarah* (1976)

SCORE 15 POINTS

FILMS OF THE EIGHTIES

How well do you know the films of the eighties?

1 What was the title of the film based on Stephen King's story of a demonic killer car?

2 Who starred opposite Jeff Bridges in the thriller *Against All Odds* (1984)?

SOLUTIONS ON PAGE 169

3 What was the title of the film Barbra Streisand directed, produced, co-wrote and starred in, which was based on a short story by the Nobel prizewinner Isaac Bashevis Singer?

4 Which top Hollywood box-office stars teamed up for the first time in *City Heat* (1985)?

5 Who directed *Curse Of The Pink Panther* (1984)?

6 Who played the title role in *Indiana Jones And The Temple Of Doom* (1984)?

7 Which pop singer featured in *Merry Christmas Mr Lawrence* (1983)?

8 Who played the title role in *Silkwood* (1984), a film of the life of Karen Silkwood, who was hailed in America as a nuclear martyr?

9 Which actor played a former West Ham and England football star in *Escape To Victory* (1981)?

10 Who gained international stardom in the title role as Roman Polanski's *Tess* (1980)?

11 Which eighties sex-symbol played Jane in *Tarzan The Ape Man* (1981)?

12 Who directed *Victor/Victoria* (1982)?

13 Which play by Harold Pinter was turned into a 1984 film starring Jeremy Irons, Ben Kingsley and Patricia Hodge?

14 What was the title of the film which re-united John Travolta and Olivia Newton John for the first time since *Grease*?

15 *Greystoke – The Legend Of Tarzan, Lord Of The Apes* (1984) was based on the novel *Tarzan Of The Apes*. Who wrote the novel?

SCORE 15 POINTS

SOLUTIONS ON PAGE 169

WHICH ONE?

Each trio of films in our list has one actor in common. Can you identify the actor who starred in all three films?

1 *Brighton Rock* (1947), *The Great Escape* (1963), *Ten Rillington Place* (1970).

2 *Hud* (1963), *The Towering Inferno* (1974), *The Verdict* (1982).

3 *The Godfather Part II* (1974), *The Deer Hunter* (1978), *Raging Bull* (1980).

4 *The Philadelphia Story* (1940), *Arsenic And Old Lace* (1944), *Charade* (1959).

5 *Stella Maris* (1918), *Pollyanna* (1924), *Little Lord Fauntleroy* (1921).

6 *Urban Cowboy* (1980), *Blow Out* (1981), *Staying Alive* (1983).

7 *Passport To Pimlico* (1949), *Murder She Said* (1961), *The VIP's* (1963).

SOLUTIONS ON PAGE 169

8 *Holiday Inn* (1942), *White Christmas* (1954), *High Society* (1956).

9 *Thoroughly Modern Millie* (1967), *Darling Lili* (1970), *Victor/Victoria* (1982).

10 *Birdman Of Alcatraz* (1961), *Kelly's Heroes* (1970), *Capricorn One* (1977).

SCORE 10 POINTS

WHO AM I DESCRIBING?

1 This Welsh-born leading actor starred in *The Longest Day* (1962) and *Exorcist II* (1977). Who am I describing?

2 This British actress (born 1946) took a special Oscar in *Pollyanna* (1960) and was with Disney for many years. Who am I describing?

3 This popular child star of the thirties and forties became U.S. Ambassador to Ghana in the seventies and then U.S. Chief of Protocol. Who am I describing?

4 He was born John Uhler in 1925 in Boston. He starred in the comic film *The Apartment* (1960) and the musical *Some Like It Hot* (1959). Who am I describing?

5 This British actor was memorable as a teenage Artful Dodger. He later became a pop star and then took to writing musicals. He has married Ann Lynn and Joan Collins. Who am I describing?

6 This British actor achieved fame in giving comic monologues. He played a memorable Long John Silver. He was knighted in 1969 and created a Lord in 1978. Who am I describing?

7 Lee Yuen Kam died in 1973 of kidney failure while making a film. He is better known by another name. Who am I describing?

8 This blonde American actress entered films via beauty contests. She was married to Burt Bacharach from 1965 to 1980. She is also known for her television film roles. Who am I describing?

SOLUTIONS ON PAGE 169

9 This actor gave memorable performances as Quasimodo, Captain Bligh, Rembrandt and Nero. Who am I describing?

10 This actor is best known for his stage roles. He appeared in *The Pink Panther Strikes Again* (1976), *Nijinsky* (1979) and *Little Lord Fauntleroy* (1980). Who am I describing?

SCORE 10 POINTS

CHILD STARS

Child stars have been popular with all generations of filmgoers. Below are some of those films in which child stars appeared. Can you complete the statements.

1 _____ _____ was immortalised in the 1920 film *The Kid* which also starred Charlie Chaplin.

2 Dawn O'Day was a popular child actress who changed her name to _____ _____ for her more 'senior' roles.

3 *Our Gang* gave us many child stars, but _____ _____ became a star in his own right after roles in *Skippy* and *The Champ*.

SOLUTIONS ON PAGE 169

4 _____ _____ left other child stars in the shadows with his thirties performance as the young David Copperfield.

5 Golden-haired _____ _____ was a star at the age of five in 1933.

6 He began on stage at the age of two and made his first film aged 6. His early roles include Puck in *A Midsummer Night's Dream* (1935) and Andy Hardy in *A Family Affair* (1937).

7 _____ _____ gained a special Academy Award for her role as *Pollyanna* (1960).

8 Born 1962, _____ _____ _____ gained an Academy Award in 1973 for *Paper Moon*.

9 _____ _____ played the young girl possessed by the devil in the 1974 film *The Exorcist*.

10 Faye Dunaway and Jon Voight played _____ _____ parents in the 1979 remake of *The Champ*.

SCORE 10 POINTS

WHO STARRED OPPOSITE ...?

For each of the following actors and actresses, can you name the person who starred opposite them in the following films?

1 Name the male actors who starred opposite Natalie Wood in the following films:
  a *Love With The Proper Stranger* (1963)   _____ _____
  b *Sex And The Single Girl* (1964)   _____ _____
  c *Inside Daisy Clover* (1965)   _____ _____

2 Name the actresses who starred opposite Steve McQueen in the following films:
  a *The War Lovers* (1962)   _____ _____ _____
  b *Bullitt* (1968)   _____ _____
  c *The Thomas Crown Affair* (1968)   _____ _____

SOLUTIONS ON PAGE 170

3 Who starred opposite Anne Bancroft in:
   a *The Slender Thread* (1966)   _____ _____
   b *The Graduate* (1968)   _____ _____
   c *The Prisoner Of Second Avenue* (1975)   _____ _____

4 Which actress starred opposite Robert Redford in:
   a *Barefoot In The Park* (1967)   _____ _____
   b *The Way We Were* (1973)   _____ _____
   c *The Great Gatsby* (1974)   _____ _____

5 Which actor starred opposite Ali McGraw in:
   a *Love Story* (1970)   _____ _____
   b *The Getaway* (1972)   _____ _____
   c *Convoy* (1978)   _____ _____

6 Name the actress who starred opposite Alan Bates in:
   a *The Shout* (1979)   _____ _____
   b *An Unmarried Woman* (1978)   _____ _____
   c *The Go-Between* (1971)   _____ _____

7 Who starred opposite Jacqueline Bisset in the following films:
   a *The Greek Tycoon* (1978)   _____ _____
   b *St. Ives* (1973)   _____ _____
   c *The Detective* (1968)   _____ _____

8 Who starred opposite Audrey Hepburn in the following films:
   a *Charade* (1963)   _____ _____
   b *My Fair Lady* (1964)   _____ _____
   c *Robin And Marion* (1976)   _____ _____

9 Who starred opposite Diane Keaton in the following films:
   a *Casablanca* (1972)   _____ _____
   b *Reds* (1981)   _____ _____
   c *Shoot The Moon* (1982)   _____ _____

10 Who starred opposite Kris Kristofferson in the following films:
   a *Alice Doesn't Live Here Any More* (1975)   _____ _____
   b *The Sailor Who Fell From Grace With The Sea* (1976)

_____
   c *A Star Is Born* (1976)   _____ _____

SCORE 10 POINTS

SOLUTIONS ON PAGE 170

DIRECTORS

Can you name the directors of the following popular films? But take care, our directors list contains one or two red herrings.

1 *Annie Hall* (1978)
2 *A Bridge Too Far* (1976)
3 *High Plains Drifter* (1972)
4 *Staying Alive* (1983)
5 *Raiders Of The Lost Ark* (1983)

6 *Ordinary People* (1980)
7 *Rosemary's Baby* (1968)
8 *International Velvet* (1976)
9 *Gregory's Girl* (1980)
10 *Reds* (1983)

Sylvester Stallone
John Ford
Robert Redford
Warren Beatty
Richard Attenborough
George Lucas

Roman Polanski
Bryan Forbes
Bill Forsyth
Woody Allen
Steven Spielberg
Clint Eastwood

SCORE 10 POINTS

THE WESTERNS

Can you shoot out the answers to the following 'Western' questions? There are two points for each correct answer.

1 Who was the actor who played the man with no name in the 'Dollars' films?

2 Can you name the actors who starred in *Butch Cassidy And The Sundance Kid* (1969)?

3 Who was the famous outlaw portrayed in *The Left-Handed Gun* (1958)?

4 He was shot in *High Noon* (1952), hanged in *The Tin Star* (1957) and knifed in *Gunfight At The OK Corral* (1957), and was the sinister co-star in *For A Few Dollars More* (1965). Who was the actor?

5 Which two distinguished actors played the gunfighter adventurers in *Vera Cruz* (1953)?

SOLUTIONS ON PAGE 170

6 Who directed *The Good, The Bad And The Ugly* (1966)?

7 Who played the Mexican bandit and the ex-IRA explosives expert who joined forces to rob a bank in *A Fistful Of Dynamite* (1971)?

8 Who were the two rival gangs in *A Fistful Of Dollars* (1964)?

9 Which actor played the blue-eyed Sheriff in *My Darling Clementine* (1946) and the blue-eyed killer in *Once Upon A Time In The West* (1969)?

10 Who gained an Oscar for his role in *Viva Zapata* (1952)?

SCORE 20 POINTS

PUBLICITY

Are you able to identify the 80's films described below from their publicity? To help you the names of some of the stars are also given.

1 'They came, They saw, They did a Little Shopping'.
Griff Rhys Jones, Mel Smith

SOLUTIONS ON PAGE 171

2 'She was a woman of Alan's dreams. She had large dark eyes, a beautiful smile and a great pair of fins'.
Tom Hanks, Daryl Hannah

3 'The new police recruits. Call them what you like ... just don't call them when you're in trouble'.
Steve Guttenberg, Kim Cattrall

4 'He taught him the secret to karate lies in the mind and heart. Not in the hands'.
Ralph Macchio, Noriyuki

5 'Could he choose between the family he always loved and the son he never knew was his?'
Martin Sheen, Blythe Danner

6 'His triumph changed the world forever'.
Ben Kingsley

7 'The most wanted man in Wakefield Prison is the Warden!'
Robert Redford

8 'The power of evil is no longer in the hands of a child'.
Sam Neill, Rossano Brazzi

9 'The closest you'll ever get to knowing the secrets of the legendary S.A.S.
Lewis Collins, Richard Widmark

10 'The most devastating Soviet killing machine ever built ... his job ... steal it'.
Clint Eastwood, Freddie Jones

11 'I race cars, I play tennis, I fondle women but I have weekends off and I am my own boss ...'.
Dudley Moore, Liza Minelli

12 'You'll root for them all ... but you'll never guess who wins'.
Burt Reynolds, Farrah Fawcett

13 'Fasten your seat belts! for a ride you'll never forget'.
Robert Hays, Julie Hagerty

SOLUTIONS ON PAGE 171

14 'They're Here'.
Jobeth Williams, Craig T. Nelson

15 'Is it a game or is it real'.
Matthew Broderick, Dabney Coleman

SCORE 15 POINTS

EPICS

Can you complete the following statements concerning epic films by filling in the blanks?

1 *Spartacus* (1960) had a star-studded cast, among them were _____ _____ as the ancient Roman nobleman, Crassus; _____ _____ as the opportunist slave dealer and _____ _____ as the cunning senator Gracchus.

2 The Biblical epic _____ _____ (1953) starring Richard Burton and Jean Simmons was the first film made in CinemaScope. (The images projected were two-and-a-half times as wide as they were high, replacing the usual square projection.)

3 _____ (1963), which began as a modestly-budgeted spectacle, became the most expensive film made at that time, after changes in actors and directors, actors' illnesses and lawsuits.

4. _____ _____ played the centurion who uttered the line 'This truly was the sahn of Gahd' in *The Greatest Story Ever Told* (1965).

5 *Ben Hur* (1959) won eleven Hollywood Oscars, among them _____ _____ for Best Actor and _____ _____ for Best Supporting Actor.

6 _____ _____ wrote *Gone With The Wind* which became an all-time film favourite, starring Clark Gable and Vivien Leigh.

7 'Whither goest thou?' is a translation of _____ _____, which was an epic concerning a Roman commander who fell in love with a Christian girl.

SOLUTIONS ON PAGE 171

8 _____ _____ _____ was a British archaeologist, soldier and author who helped organize the Arab revolt against the Turks in World War 1. His story was told in the 1962 epic _____ _____ _____.

9 'The Falcon And The Dove' was the song from the epic _____ _____ (1961). It was nominated for an Academy Award.

10 *How The West Was Won* (1962) told the life story of the daughter of a pioneering family from youth to old age. Its star-studded cast included _____ _____ as the narrator.

SCORE 10 POINTS

SONGS IN FILMS 2

Can you identify the films from which the following songs were taken?

1 'Thank Heaven For Little Girls'
2 'No More Lonely Nights'
3 'I Just Called To Say I Love You'
4 'Talk To The Animals'

SOLUTIONS ON PAGE 171

5 'Food, Glorious Food'
6 'Oh, What A Beautiful Morning'
7 'Edelweiss'
8 'The Pusher'
9 'Songs Of Life'
10 'Raindrops Keep Fallin' On My Head'

⟶SCORE 10 POINTS

SKELETON QUIZ

The first clue gives the central vertical of the puzzle, the others give all the horizontal lines. Once you have answered question one correctly, your task will be much easier.

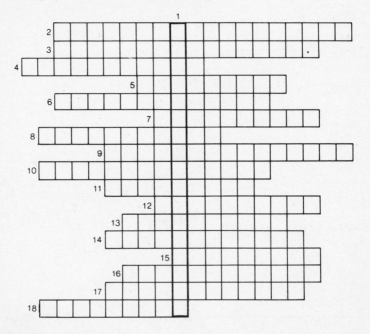

CLUES
1 Jack Nicholson gained an Oscar for this film of 1983
2 Rupert Everett and Miranda Richardson starred in this 1985 film of the life of Ruth Ellis

SOLUTIONS ON PAGE 171

3 Julie Andrews portrayed this character in *Star* (1968)

4 He replaced John Travolta in the title role of *American Gigolo* (1979)

5 He played Sonny Corleone in *The Godfather* (1972)

6 He played a tough cowboy-cop in *Coogan's Bluff* (1968)

7 This American singer starred in *'Oh, God!'* (1977)

8 He directed *The Killing Fields* (1985)

9 He directed *Gremlins* (1984)

10 She played the title role in *The One And Only Original Phyllis Dixey* (1978)

11 He directed *A Passage To India* (1985)

12 He was the male star in *Footloose* (1984)

13 She was the Acid Queen in *Tommy* (1975)

14 A gormless gardener was his role in *Being There* (1980)

15 She starred with Woody Allen in *Zelig* (1984) and *Broadway Danny Rose* (1984)

16 He played a saxophone ace in *New York, New York* (1977)

17 He proclaimed 'The British are coming . . .' after accepting his Oscar in 1983

18 He played 'Milo Mindbender' in *Catch 22* (1970)

SCORE 18 POINTS

A QUESTION OF LISTS 2

In each of the following questions a number of answers are required. We give one answer, can you complete the remainder?

1 Sidney Poitier starred in *The Blackboard Jungle* (1955). Can you complete the titles of some of his other popular films?
Lilies _____ _____ _____ (1963)
To Sir _____ _____ (1967)
Guess _____ _____ _____ _____ (1967)

2 Which star of *Return Of The Jedi* (1983), *The Empire Strikes Back* (1980) and *Star Wars* (1977) has a famous singing father and acting mother?
star of the films   _____ _____
father   _____ _____
mother   Debbie Reynolds

SOLUTIONS ON PAGE 172

3 Who played opposite Faye Dunaway in the following films?
Bonnie And Clyde (1967)   Warren Beatty
The Thomas Crown Affair
(1968)   _____ _____
Chinatown (1974)   _____ _____
Network (1976)   _____ _____

4 Can you name the actors who played the title roles of *The Good, The Bad And The Ugly* (1966)?
Eli Wallach

_____ _____

_____ _____ _____

5 Can you name the other half of the machismo teams in these eras?
Thirties   Spencer Tracy and Clark Gable
Fifties   Burt Lancaster and _____ _____
Seventies   Paul Newman and _____ _____

6 *Alice's Adventures In Wonderland* (1972) was a popular film with a star-studded cast. Can you identify the actors who played the following roles?
Alice   Fiona Fullerton
White Rabbit _____ _____
Dormouse   _____ _____
Gryphon   _____ _____
March Hare   _____ _____

SOLUTIONS ON PAGE 172

7 Warren Beatty starred opposite Eva Marie Saint in *All Fall Down* (1962). Who starred opposite him in
The Roman Spring Of Mrs Stone (1961)
The Only Game In Town (1969)
Reds (1981)

8 The Von Trapp family from *The Sound Of Music* (1965) included seven children. Can you name them?
Kurt ＿＿＿
＿＿＿ ＿＿＿
＿＿＿ ＿＿＿
＿＿＿

9 Which actresses played the following 'Bond' girls?
Pussy Galore in *Goldfinger*
(1964)　　　　　　　　　　Honor Blackman
Mary Goodnight in *The Man*
With The Golden Gun (1974)　＿＿＿ ＿＿＿
Honey Ryder in *Dr No* (1962)　＿＿＿ ＿＿＿
Domino in *Thunderball*
(1965)　　　　　　　　　　＿＿＿ ＿＿＿
Tiffany Case in *Diamonds*
Are Forever (1971)　　　　　＿＿＿ ＿＿＿ ＿＿＿
Solitaire in *Live And Let Die*
(1973)　　　　　　　　　　＿＿＿ ＿＿＿

SOLUTIONS ON PAGE 172

10 Who was awarded the Best Actor Oscar for the following films?
In The Heat Of The Night
(1967)   Rod Steiger
Save The Tiger (1973)   ____ ____
Tender Mercies (1984)   ____ ____
Raging Bull (1980)   ____ ____ ____

SCORE 10 POINTS

SOLUTIONS ON PAGE 172

A QUESTION OF LISTS

1 *East Of Eden* (1955), *Rebel Without A Cause* (1956).

2 In 1954 Marilyn Monroe married Joe Di Maggio and in 1956, Arthur Miller.

3 *A Touch Of Class* (1972)   George Segal
Bequest To The Nation
(1973)   Peter Finch
House Calls (1978)   Walter Matthau

4 *To Be Or Not To Be* (1983) Mel Brooks and Anne Bancroft
Harry And Son (1984)   Paul Newman and
   Joanne Woodward

5 John Travolta played Danny Zuko in *Grease* (1978) and Bud Davis in *Urban Cowboy* (1980).

6 *Road To Zanzibar* (1941), *Road To Morocco* (1942), *Road To Utopia* (1945), *Road To Rio* (1947) and *Road To Bali* (1952).

7 Adolph Arthur became Harpo, Leonard became Chico and Herbert became Zeppo.

8 Dr Zhivago   Boris Pasternak
Dr Dolittle   Hugh Lofting
Dr Faustus   Christopher Marlowe
Doctor In The House   Richard Gordon

9 *Scrooge*   *A Christmas Carol*
Mr Quilp   *The Old Curiosity Shop*

10 *The Wild One*   Marlon Brando
*Saturday Night And
Sunday Morning*   Albert Finney

FILM THEMES

1	*Kramer v Kramer*	(D)
2	*Harry And Tonto*	(J)
3	*Willard*	(A)

4	*Papillon*	(F)
5	*A Day In The Death Of Joe Egg*	(B)
6	*Barry Lyndon*	(I)
7	*Norma Rae*	(C)
8	*The China Syndrome*	(E)
9	*Reds*	(H)
10	*Raiders Of The Lost Ark*	(G)

SPORTING FILMS

1 Pool   Omar Sharif, Bruce Boxleitner and James Coburn starred in this film about the adventures of some pool sharks.

2 Boxing   This film was a remake of a 1931 film of the same name, involving a young boy who has confidence in a washed-up fighter. The 1931 version was nominated for an Oscar. The 1979 version starred Jon Voight, Faye Dunaway and Ricky Schroeder.

3 Horse Racing   John Hurt played the jockey Bob Champion who conquered cancer and went on to win the Grand National on Aldaniti.

4 Cycling   *Breaking Away* was an unexpected smash success, shot with unknown actors on location in Bloomington, Indiana.

5 Ice Hockey   Paul Newman was the star of this violent comedy about a player coach and his fading hockey team.

6 Athletics   *Chariots Of Fire* won Oscars for best picture, music and costume design. It told the story of the rivalry between Harold Abraham and Eric Liddell in the 1924 Paris Olympics.

7 Football   Burt Reynolds and Kris Kristofferson were the stars of this film about a football manager's daughter who has to decide between two star members of the team.

8 Formula-1 Motor Racing   Al Pacino played the motor-racing driver in love with a girl with a terminal illness.

9 Tennis   Ali McGraw and Dean-Paul Martin were the stars of *Players* which was set around a Wimbledon match.

10 Baseball   Walter Matthau and Tatum O'Neal starred in this sentimental comedy about an ex-baseball professional who coaches a team of tough kids.

☆ ☆ ☆ ☆ ☆ **BONUS TIME** ☆ ☆ ☆ ☆ ☆

1 Audrey Hepburn
2 Diane Keaton
3 Susan George and
  Peter Fonda
4 Omar Sharif
5 *The Hunter*
6 *Dr Strangelove*
7 Alec Guinness
8 Sidney Greenstreet
9 Olivia Hussey
10 Joan Crawford
11 Sting from The Police
12 David Niven
13 Tom Conti
14 Britt Ekland
15 Tatum O'Neal

OSCARS

1 Shirley Maclaine
2 'What A Feeling'
3 Audrey Hepburn
4 Jane Fonda. *Klute* (1971) and *Coming Home* (1978)
5 Sissy Spacek
6 *The King And I*
7 George C Scott. *Patton* (1969)
8 Ingrid Bergman
9 *Network*
10 Vivien Leigh

FAMOUS FILM ACTORS – AND THEIR TELEVISION ROLES

1 Ryan O'Neal
2 Telly Savalas
3 Lee Remick
4 Ali McGraw
5 Glenda Jackson
6 James Garner
7 Clint Eastwood
8 Julie Christie
9 Jane Wyman
10 Howard Keel

HORROR

1 *An American Werewolf In London*
2 *The Devil Rides Out*
3 *The Texas Chainsaw Massacre*
4 *Rosemary's Baby*
5 *The Postman Always Rings Twice*
6 *Dr Jekyll And Mr Hyde*
7 *Amityville II: The Possession*
8 *Whatever Happened To Baby Jane?*

9 *Dressed To Kill*
10 *The Spiral Staircase*

SCIENCE FICTION

1 *The Sentinel.*
2 *Poltergeist.*
3 Richard Dreyfuss.
4 You could have had any of the following: Charlton Heston, Kim Hunter, Roddy McDowall, James Daly, Linda Harrison, Maurice Evans, James Whitmore.
5 Elliott.
6 *Indiana Jones And The Temple Of Doom.*
7 R2-D2 and C-3PO.
8 John Williams.
9 *The Wrath Of Khan.*
10 Stanley Kubrick.

SONGS IN FILMS

1 *A Star Is Born* (1976)
2 *The Wizard Of Oz* (1939)
3 *White Christmas* (1954)
4 *Mary Poppins* (1964)
5 *Purple Rain* (1984)
6 *Cabaret* (1973)
7 *Grease* (1978)
8 *The Rose* (1979)
9 *Ghostbusters* (1984)
10 *The King And I* (1956)
11 *Paint Your Wagon* (1970)
12 *Breakfast At Tiffany's* (1961)
13 *The Graduate* (1967)
14 *My Fair Lady* (1964)
15 *West Side Story* (1961)

JAMES BOND

1 Bernard Lee
2 Ian Fleming
3 *The Spy Who Loved Me,* Carly Simon
4 *Dr No*
5 Oddjob
6 *Never Say Never Again*
7 M
8 Goldfinger
9 Q
10 *Casino Royale*
11 Miss Moneypenny
12 Japan
13 Special Executive for Terrorism, Revolution and Espionage
14 George Lazenby
15 Christopher Lee
16 *Live And Let Die*
17 *Moonraker*
18 Jaws
19 *For Your Eyes Only* (1981)
20 Donald Pleasance

IN COMMON

1 They both had alcoholism as their theme.
2 They were all voted the World's Worst Dressed Women in 1972.
3 Katharine Hepburn was awarded Best-Actress Oscars for each of these films.
4 They are all directed by Robert Altman.
5 They were all films chosen for the Royal Command Performance.
6 They were all biographies of famous painters: *Lust For Life* – van Gogh; *The Moon And Sixpence* – Gauguin; *The Agony And The Ecstacy* – Michaelangelo.
7 John Wayne died in all of them.
8 They are all Sherlock Holmes films.
9 All starred the American folk and rock singer Kris Kristofferson.
10 All starred members of the Fonda family. *Klute* – Jane Fonda, *Easy Rider* – Peter Fonda, *On Golden Pond* – Henry Fonda, Jane Fonda.
11 The characters were shipwrecked.
12 All directed by Mel Brooks.
13 It was Marni Nixon's singing voice that was dubbed in for Audrey Hepburn in *My Fair Lady* and also for Natalie Wood in *West Side Story*.
14 They have all played Batman.
15 They were all schoolteachers before they became actors.

FILM CHARACTERS

1 Daddy Warbucks was the millionaire munitions factory owner who appeared in *Annie* (1982). Albert Finney played this role.
2 *Terms Of Endearment* (1984). Shirley Maclaine played Aurora Greenway in this Oscar winning film.
3 Caractacus Potts was a character from the popular children's film *Chitty Chitty Bang Bang* (1968). This role was played by Dick Van Dyke.
4 John Travolta played Jack Terry in the 1983 thriller *Blow Out*.
5 Fast Eddie Felson was a character played by Paul Newman in *The Hustler* (1961).
6 Selina was a character in the blockbuster film *Supergirl*.
7 Popeye Doyle was the New York cop who tracked a drugs ring in *The French Connection* (1971) and *French Connection II* (1975).
8 Mrs Robinson was a character from *The Graduate* played by Anne Bancroft. She was the subject of one of the Simon and Garfunkel songs from the film.

9 Esther Hoffman Howard, played by Barbra Streisand, became a star in the 1976 version of *A Star Is Born*.

10 Mr Bunnies and Mr McCools were the rival ice-cream companies in the frosty family-feud film, *Comfort And Joy* by Bill Forsyth.

WHO SAID THAT . . .?

1 Al Jolson in *The Jazz Singer* (1927)
2 Ryan O'Neal in *Love Story* (1970)
3 Bugs Bunny
4 Humphrey Bogart in *Casablanca* (1942)
5 James Cagney
6 Clark Gable in *Gone With The Wind* (1939)
7 Greta Garbo
8 Rex Harrison in *My Fair Lady* (1964)
9 Said about W. C. Fields
10 Marlon Brando in *On The Waterfront* (1954)

STAGE NAMES

1 Julie Andrews
2 Richard Burton
3 Tony Curtis
4 Doris Day
5 Sophia Loren
6 Marilyn Monroe
7 Cliff Richard
8 Shelley Winters
9 John Wayne
10 Ginger Rogers

A MIXED BAG

1 *Twist Around The Clock* (1961)
2 Charlie Chaplin
3 Ellen Burstyn was nominated for an Oscar in all of them.
4 Clapperboard
5 *West Side Story* (1961)
6 *Lord Of The Flies* (1963)
7 The Von Trapp family
8 Douglas Fairbanks Sr.
9 *Reach For The Sky* (1956)
10 Artie Shaw

CHARACTER TYPES

1 Ice maiden — Ursula Andress
2 Macho tough guy — Charles Bronson
3 King of British horror — Christopher Lee
4 International heart-throb — Omar Sharif
5 Dance king — John Travolta

6	The modern American urban man	George Segal
7	The modern Chaplin	Woody Allen
8	The Sundance Kid	Robert Redford
9	Working-class hero	Albert Finney
10	French gangster	Alain Delon

GREAT MALE LOVERS OF THE SCREEN

1 John Travolta
2 Rudolf Valentino
3 Clint Eastwood
4 Robert Redford
5 Steve McQueen
6 Marlon Brando
7 Rock Hudson
8 Sylvester Stallone
9 Robert De Niro
10 Sean Connery
11 Paul Newman
12 Ryan O'Neal
13 Kris Kristofferson
14 Dustin Hoffman
15 Burt Reynolds

DISNEY SONGS

1 *Cinderella* (1950), The Fairy Godmother's Song.
2 *Mary Poppins* (1964)
3 *Snow White And The Seven Dwarfs* (1937)
4 *Pinocchio* (1940)
5 *The Three Little Pigs* (1933)
6 *Jungle Book* (1967)
7 *Bambi* (1942)
8 *Lady And The Tramp* (1955)
9 *The Slipper And The Rose* (1976)
10 *Song Of The South* (1947)

WHAT A LAUGH!

1 Charlie Chaplin
2 Harold Lloyd
3 W. C. Fields
4 Burt Reynolds
5 *It's A Mad, Mad, Mad, Mad World*
6 Woody Allen
7 Peter Sellers
8 Doris Day and Rock Hudson
9 *Trading Places*
10 *Splash*

HITCHCOCK – THE MASTER OF SUSPENSE

1 *The Thirty-nine Steps*   2 *Blackmail*

3 *Jamaica Inn*
4 Laurence Olivier
5 *Dial M For Murder*
6 *To Catch A Thief*
7 *Vertigo*
8 *North By Northwest*
9 Norman Bates in *Psycho*
10 *Torn Curtain*

BINGO

1 Balboa
2 Rooster Cogburn
3 Father Lamont
4 Kirk Douglas
5 *Any Which Way You Can* (1980)
6 *Scum* (1979)
7 *The African Queen* (1951)
8 David Niven
9 *The Daily Planet*
10 Zsa Zsa Gabor
11 Mario Lanza
12 Morlocks
13 Dustin Hoffman
14 *On Golden Pond* (1981)
15 *Dr Jekyll And Mr Hyde*
16 Bo Derek
17 Discovery
18 Jules Verne
19 *South Pacific* (1958)
20 Richard Chamberlain
21 Mel Brooks
22 'Old Man River'
23 *Mary Poppins* (1964)
24 Chicago
25 James Stewart
26 Quasimodo
27 Michael Caine
28 *The St Valentine's Day Massacre*
29 *Oliver's Story* (1978)
30 Christopher Lee

TRUE LIFE STORIES

1	*Brother Sun, Sister Moon*	St Francis of Assisi
2	*The Music Lovers*	Tchaikovsky
3	*The Elephant Man*	Joseph Merrick
4	*The Spirit Of St Louis*	Charles Lindberg (aviator who made the first solo transatlantic flight)
5	*Running Brave*	Billy Mills (Sioux indian who won the 10,000 metres for America in the 1964 Olympics)
6	*A Song Of Summer*	Frederick Delius (composer)
7	*A Man For All Seasons*	Sir Thomas More
8	*The Miracle Worker*	Helen Keller
9	*Ten Rillington Place*	John Reginald Christie, the forties murderer
10	*The Inn Of The Sixth Happiness*	Gladys Aylward (English girl who became a missionary in China)

11 *Annie Get Your Gun* — Annie Oakley
12 *Funny Girl* — Fanny Brice (Jewish singer/comedienne)
13 *Lady Sings The Blues* — Billie Holiday (jazz singer)
14 *Stevie* — Stevie Smith (poet)
15 *The Incredible Sarah* — Sarah Bernhardt (great tragic actress)

FILMS OF THE EIGHTIES

1 *Christine* (1984)
2 Rachel Ward
3 *Yentl* (1984)
4 Clint Eastwood and Burt Reynolds
5 Blake Edwards
6 Harrison Ford
7 David Bowie
8 Meryl Streep
9 Michael Caine
10 Nastassia Kinski
11 Bo Derek
12 Blake Edwards
13 *Betrayal*
14 *Two Of A Kind* (1984)
15 Edgar Rice Burroughs

WHICH ONE?

1 Richard Attenborough
2 Paul Newman
3 Robert De Niro
4 Cary Grant
5 Mary Pickford
6 John Travolta
7 Margaret Rutherford
8 Bing Crosby
9 Julie Andrews
10 Telly Savalas

WHO AM I DESCRIBING?

1 Richard Burton
2 Hayley Mills
3 Shirley Temple
4 Jack Lemmon
5 Anthony Newley
6 Bernard Miles
7 Bruce Lee
8 Angie Dickinson
9 Charles Laughton
10 Colin Blakely

CHILD STARS

1 Jackie Coogan
2 Anne Shirley
3 Jackie Cooper
4 Freddie Bartholemew
5 Shirley Temple
6 Mickey Rooney
7 Hayley Mills
8 Tatum O'Neal
9 Linda Blair
10 Ricky Shroeder

WHO STARRED OPPOSITE

1 **a** Steve McQueen
  b Tony Curtis
  c Robert Redford

2 **a** Shirley Anne Field
  b Jacqueline Bisset
  c Faye Dunaway

3 **a** Sidney Poitier
  b Dustin Hoffman
  c Jack Lemmon

4 **a** Jane Fonda
  b Barbra Streisand
  c Mia Farrow

5 **a** Ryan O'Neil
  b Steve McQueen
  c Kris Kristofferson

6 **a** Susannah York
  b Jill Clayburgh
  c Julie Christie

7 **a** Anthony Quinn
  b Charles Bronson
  c Frank Sinatra

8 **a** Cary Grant
  b Rex Harrison
  c Sean Connery

9 **a** Al Pacino
  b Warren Beatty
  c Albert Finney

10 **a** Ellen Burstyn
  b Sarah Miles
  c Barbra Streisand

DIRECTORS

1 Woody Allen
2 Richard Attenborough
3 Clint Eastwood
4 Sylvester Stallone
5 Steven Spielberg
6 Robert Redford
7 Roman Polanski
8 Bryan Forbes
9 Bill Forsyth
10 Warren Beatty

THE WESTERNS

1 Clint Eastwood
2 Paul Newman –
  Butch Cassidy
  Robert Redford –
  Sundance Kid
3 Billy The Kid
4 Lee Van Cleef
5 Burt Lancaster
  Gary Cooper
6 Sergio Leoni
7 Rod Steiger
  James Coburn
8 The Baxters and The Rojos
9 Henry Fonda
10 Anthony Quinn

PUBLICITY

1 *Morons From Outer Space*
2 *Splash*
3 *Police Academy*
4 *The Karate Kid*
5 *Man, Woman And Child*
6 *Gandhi*
7 *Brubaker*
8 *The Final Conflict*
9 *Who Dares Wins*
10 *Firefox*

11 *Arthur*
12 *The Cannonball Run*
13 *Airplane II The Sequel*
14 *Poltergeist*
.15 *War Games*

EPICS

1 **a** Laurence Olivier, **b** Peter Ustinov, **c** Charles Laughton.
2 *The Robe*
3 *Cleopatra*
4 John Wayne
5 Charlton Heston (Best Actor), Hugh Griffith (Best Supporting Actor).
6 Margaret Mitchell
7 *Quo Vadis?*
8 Thomas Edward Lawrence. *Lawrence Of Arabia.*
9 *El Cid*
10 Spencer Tracy

SONGS IN FILMS 2

1 *Gigi* (1958)
2 *Give My Regards To Broad Street* (1984)
3 *The Woman In Red* (1984)
4 *Doctor Dolittle* (1967)
5 *Oliver!* (1968)
6 *Oklahoma* (1955)
7 *The Sound Of Music* (1965)
8 *Easy Rider* (1969)
9 *The Jazz Singer* (1980)
10 *Butch Cassidy And The Sundance Kid* (1969)

SKELETON QUIZ

1 Terms Of Endearment
2 Dance With A Stranger
3 Gertrude Lawrence
4 Richard Gere
5 James Caan
6 Clint Eastwood
7 John Denver
8 Roland Joffe
9 Steven Spielberg
10 Lesley Anne Down
11 David Lean
12 Kevin Bacon
13 Tina Turner
14 Peter Sellers
15 Mia Farrow
16 Robert de Niro
17 Colin Welland
18 Jon Voight

A QUESTION OF LISTS 2

1 *Lilies Of The Field*
To Sir With Love
Guess Who's Coming To Dinner

2 Carrie Fisher was a star from *The Empire Strikes Back* and *Star Wars*. Her father was Eddie Fisher.

3 *The Thomas Crown Affair*
(1968)   Steve McQueen
Chinatown (1974)   Jack Nicholson
Network (1976)   William Holden

4 Clint Eastwood
Lee Van Cleef

5 Burt Lancaster and Kirk Douglas
Paul Newman and Robert Redford

6 White Rabbit   Michael Crawford
Dormouse   Dudley Moore
Gryphon   Spike Milligan
March Hare   Peter Sellers

7 *The Roman Spring Of Mrs Stone* Vivian Leigh
The Only Game In Town   Elizabeth Taylor
Reds   Diane Keaton

8 Kurt   Liesl
Friedrich   Brigitta
Marta   Gretl
Louisa

9 Mary Goodnight was played by Britt Ekland
Honey Ryder by   Ursula Andress
Domino by   Claudine Auger

Tiffany Case by   Jill St John
Solitaire by   Jane Seymour

10 *Save The Tiger*   Jack Lemmon
Tender Mercies   Robert Duvall
Raging Bull   Robert De Niro

How well did you do?
*Maximum score 438. If you scored
more than 200 – take a bow; more
than 250 – treat yourself to a night out;
over 300 – have an Oscar.*

Books

I n this section we have concentrated on popular literature which has been adapted for either the large or the small screen so, although you may not have read the book, you have a good chance of being familiar with its contents. Classic novels as well as today's bestsellers are included in the section, so there is something here for all the family.

Are you a detective fan? Then you will be able to solve the confusion in the 'Detectives And Their Creators' quiz. Maybe nostalgia is more your line, then 'Memories Are Made of This' is for you; the younger members of the family may be able to give you some help with this. Perhaps you are an avid reader of the block-buster novel. If so, 'Bestsellers' is your quiz. We hope you enjoy the quizzes as much you enjoyed the books themselves.

SPOT THE MISTAKES

Can you spot the mistakes on each of the following books?

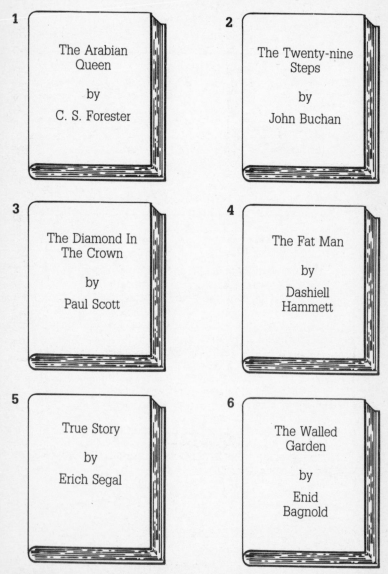

1

The Arabian
Queen

by

C. S. Forester

2

The Twenty-nine
Steps

by

John Buchan

3

The Diamond In
The Crown

by

Paul Scott

4

The Fat Man

by

Dashiell
Hammett

5

True Story

by

Erich Segal

6

The Walled
Garden

by

Enid
Bagnold

SOLUTIONS ON PAGE 187

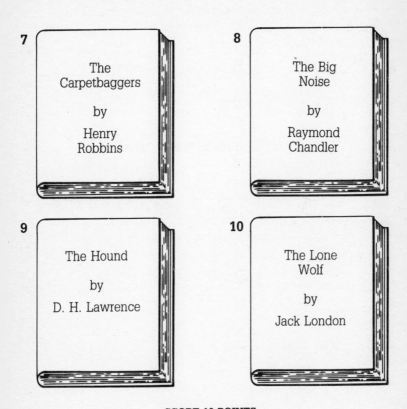

7 The Carpetbaggers

by

Henry Robbins

8 The Big Noise

by

Raymond Chandler

9 The Hound

by

D. H. Lawrence

10 The Lone Wolf

by

Jack London

SCORE 10 POINTS

BOOK TITLES

Can you complete the titles of the following famous books which were all made into popular films?

1 _____ _____ *File* — Frederick Forsyth
2 _____ *People* — Judith Guest
3 *The* _____ *Has* _____ — Jack Higgins
4 *The History* _____ _____ — H. G. Wells
_____

SOLUTIONS ON PAGE 187

5 *Journey To _____ _____*   Jules Verne
_____ _____ _____
6 *The _____ Wives*   Ira Levin
7 *They Shoot _____ _____*   Horace McCoy
_____?
8 *All The _____ _____*   Carl Bernstein and
                                     Bob Woodward
9 *Adolf Hitler – My _____*   Spike Milligan
_____ _____ _____
10 *A Kind _____ _____*   Stan Barstow

SCORE 10 POINTS

BONUS QUESTIONS

1 *The Grass Is Singing* was adapted for film in 1982 and starred Karen Black and John Thaw. Who wrote this novel set in Africa?

SOLUTIONS ON PAGE 188

★★★★★★★★★★★★★★★★★★★★★★★★★★★★★★

2 *The Country Girl* (1984) was a nostalgic title about a Catholic girlhood in the 1950s. Who wrote the novel?

3 Which leader in the horror-story field had his book *The Dead Zone* adapted for film in 1984?

4 Which novel by Edgar Rice Burroughs told of survivors from a torpedoed supply ship who encountered an island full of pre-historic monsters?

5 Linsey Beauchamp and Peter Davison played the central characters in a BBC adaptation of which Arnold Bennett story?

SCORE 2 POINTS FOR EACH CORRECT ANSWER

★★★★★★★★★★★★★★★★★★★★★★★★★★★★★★

DETECTIVES AND THEIR CREATORS

Can you pair the detective with his or her creator?

Detectives	*Creators*
1 Inspector Maigret	G. K. Chesterton
2 Miss Marple	Raymond Chandler
3 Nero Wolfe	Earl Derr Biggers
4 Philip Marlowe	Dorothy L. Sayers
5 Sherlock Holmes	Dashiell Hammett
6 Father Brown	Georges Simenon
7 Charlie Chan	Agatha Christie
8 Ellery Queen	Rex Stout
9 Lord Peter Wimsey	Sir Arthur Conan Doyle
10 Continental Op	Manfred B. Lee and
	Frederick Dannay

SCORE 10 POINTS

CHARACTERS FROM CLASSIC NOVELS

Below are listed a number of characters who all appear in the same classic novel, can you identify the book and the author? All of the books have been serialised for television.

1 Rudolf Rassendyll, 'Black' Michael, Rupert of Hentzau

SOLUTIONS ON PAGE 188

2 Mr Heathcliff, Hindley, Miss Linton
3 Mr Bingley, Elizabeth Bennett, Mr Darcy
4 Natasha, Prince Vasili, Prince Nikolai, Andreyevich Bolkonsky
5 Sue Bridehead, Jude Fawley, Mr Troutham
6 Badger, Rat, Mole
7 Walter Morel, Mrs Leivers, Clara
8 Mr Squeers, Sir Matthew Pupker, Mr Snawley
9 Septimus Harding, Mrs Proudie, Dr Grantly
10 Dundridge, Ganglion, Densher

SCORE 10 POINTS

BESTSELLERS

Many books from the 'bestseller' lists have been adapted for television. Can you identify the books and their authors from the characters given? A list of books to choose from is given below.

1 Jamie McGregor, Mr Blackwell, Kate
2 Paddy Cleary, Ralph de Bricassart, Meggie
3 Janna Roslyn, Laurence Castallack, Jan-Yves
4 Emma Harte, Edwin Fairley, Paul McGill
5 Maxine, Pagan, Aunt Hortense
6 Chicken George, Kunta Kinte, Kizzy

SOLUTIONS ON PAGE 189

7 Helen Lawson, Ann Welles, Jennifer North
8 Maggy Lunel, Teddy, Fauve
9 Maryann Flood, Mike Keys, Ross
10 Byron Henry, Natalie Jastrow and Victor Henry

Lace	*The Winds Of War*
Roots	*The Thornbirds*
Valley Of The Dolls	*79 Park Avenue*
Master Of The Game	*Mistral's Daughter*
Penmarric	*A Woman Of Substance*

SCORE 10 POINTS (20 points if you don't look at the list)

THE LIVES OF ACTORS

Can you identify the actors whose lives are portrayed in the following books? We have given a list for you to choose from.

1 *Golden Boy* (1984)
2 *Shelley* (1980)
3 *P.S. I Love You* (1983)
4 *Love, Curiosity, Freckles And Doubt* (1984)
5 *Before I Forget* (1983)
6 *This Is My Song* (1984)
7 *I Like What I Know* (1958)
8 _____ _____ *Mother Goddam* (1983)
9 *Limelight And After* (1983)
10 _____ _____ *The Reluctant Movie Queen* (1983)
11 *Raising Caine* (1983)
12 *Baby Doll* (1984)
13 _____ _____ *The Last Star* (1983)
14 *Don't Fall Off The Mountain* (1970)
15 *An Orderly Man* (1983)

Peter Sellers	Dirk Bogarde
Vincent Price	Michael Caine
Pat Phoenix	Bette Davis
Claire Bloom	Shirley Maclaine
Elizabeth Taylor	Shelley Winters
Petula Clark	Betty Grable
James Mason	Carroll Baker
William Holden	

SCORE 15 POINTS

SOLUTIONS ON PAGE 189

WHICH NOVEL?

Can you name the authors whose works were the basis for the following programmes? If you answer without referring to the list of authors below score two points. If you refer to the list score one point.

1 *Zoo Gang*
2 *Kings Royal*
3 *Sorrell And Son*
4 *Poldark*
5 *The Mallens*
6 *Testament Of Youth*
7 *Tinker, Tailor, Soldier, Spy*
8 *Man At The Top*
9 *The Saint*
10 *The Invisible Man*
11 *Rumpole Of The Bailey*
12 *Brideshead Revisited*
13 *Thomas The Tank Engine*
14 *The Barchester Chronicles*
15 *Roots*
16 *South Riding*
17 *Dr Kildare*
18 *Voyage Round My Father*
19 *The Country Diary Of An Edwardian Lady*
20 *Lace*

Warwick Deeping
Catherine Cookson
Paul Gallico
Jeffrey Archer

John Braine
John Mortimer
Alex Haley
Evelyn Waugh

SOLUTIONS ON PAGE 189

John Le Carré
Leslie Charteris
H. G. Wells
Winston Graham
Vera Brittain
John Quigley
D. H. Lawrence

Shirley Conran
Anthony Trollope
Rev. W. Awdry
Max Brand
Jane Austen
Edith Holden
Winifred Holtby

SCORE 20 POINTS (40 points without the list)

MEMORIES ARE MADE OF THIS

Can you remember the books you read as a child? Choose the correct answer from those given.

1 J. M. Barrie in his play *Peter Pan* created the characters of Wendy, Michael and John. Their surname was
 a Banks
 b Darling
 c March
 d Brown

2 *Charlie And The Chocolate Factory* was the wonderful creation of
 a Enid Blyton
 b Charles Kingsley
 c Roald Dahl
 d Beatrix Potter

3 Which little girl's adventures began when she fell down a rabbit hole?
 a Jane
 b Amy
 c Jo
 d Alice

4 By what name is Cedric Erroll more popularly known?
 a Little Lord Fauntleroy
 b Mr Plod
 c Rupert Bear
 d Huckleberry Finn

SOLUTIONS ON PAGE 190

5 Billy Bunter, known as 'the fat owl of the Remove' attended the school known as
   a Greyfriars
   b Whitefriars
   c St Trinians
   d Grange Hill

6 We learn of the character Mrs Doasyouwouldbedoneby in
   a *Gulliver's Travels*
   b *Black Beauty*
   c *Paddington*
   d *The Water Babies*

7 The bully in *Tom Brown's Schooldays* was
   a Tucker
   b Flashman
   c Tommy Brock
   d Bully Bullseye

SOLUTIONS ON PAGE 190

8 Who was the young boy who went to sea in search of Captain Flint's treasure in *Treasure Island*?
a Tom Sawyer
b Alan Humphries
c Jim Hawkins
d Ralph Strakey

9 Winnie the Pooh had a donkey friend called
a Eeyore
b Roo
c Neigh
d Mule

10 Clara Sesemann was the invalid girl in a wheelchair in the stories of
a *The Wind In The Willows*
b *The Famous Five*
c *Heidi*
d *Little Women*

SCORE 10 POINTS

THE BOOK AND THE FILM

Many great films have been adaptations of famous novels. Can you identify the authors of the following works and one of the actors who played a major role in the film version of each book. (The date refers to the film.)

1 *All Creatures Great And Small* (1974)
2 *How Green Was My Valley* (1941)
3 *The Spy Who Came In From The Cold* (1966)
4 *The Hireling* (1973)
5 *Ice Station Zebra* (1968)
6 *The Devils* (1970)
7 *The Prime Of Miss Jean Brodie* (1969)
8 *Saturday Night And Sunday Morning* (1960)
9 *The Poseidon Adventure* (1972)
10 *Airport* (1969)
11 *The French Lieutenant's Woman* (1981)

SOLUTIONS ON PAGE 190

12 *One Flew Over The Cuckoo's Nest* (1975)
13 *To Kill A Mockingbird* (1962)
14 *The Day Of The Jackal* (1973)
15 *The Godfather* (1971)

SCORE 30 POINTS

SOLUTIONS ON PAGE 190

SPOT THE MISTAKES

1 *The African Queen* by C. S. Forester
2 *The Thirty-nine Steps* by John Buchan
3 *The Jewel In The Crown* by Paul Scott
4 *The Thin Man* by Dashiell Hammett
5 *Love Story* by Erich Segal
6 *The Chalk Garden* by Enid Bagnold
7 *The Carpetbaggers* by Harold Robbins
8 *The Big Sleep* by Raymond Chandler
9 *The Fox* by D. H. Lawrence
10 *The Sea Wolf* by Jack London

BOOK TITLES

1 *The Odessa File.* Jon Voight starred as the young German reporter who hunts down a gang of Nazis in the 1978 adaptation of Frederick Forsyth's novel.

2 *Ordinary People* by Judith Guest was adapted for film in 1980 and starred Donald Sutherland and Mary Tyler Moore. It received Oscars for Best Film and Best Director (Robert Redford).

3 *The Eagle Has Landed.* Michael Caine, Donald Sutherland, Robert Duvall and Donald Pleasance were among the many stars who appeared in this adaptation of Higgins' spy story.

4 *The History Of Mr Polly.* The 1949 version of this popular comic novel starred John Mills, Sally Ann Howes and Megs Jenkins.

5 *Journey To The Centre Of The Earth.* The 1959 version of this fantastic tale starred James Mason and Pat Boone.

6 *The Stepford Wives.* Husbands replace their wives with computerized models in this novel, adapted for film in 1974.

7 *They Shoot Horses, Don't They?* Tragedy during a marathon dance in the early thirties was the theme of this book, adapted for film in 1969.

8 *All The President's Men* was a reconstruction of the Watergate Scandal by two reporters on the *Washington Post*. The film (1976) starred Robert Redford and Dustin Hoffman.

9 *Adolf Hitler – My Part In His Downfall*. Spike Milligan memoirs. Spike played his own father in the 1972 film.

10 *A Kind Of Loving* by Stan Barstow was adapted for film in 1962 and starred Alan Bates, June Ritchie and Thora Hird.

☆ ☆ ☆ ☆ **BONUS QUESTIONS** ☆ ☆ ☆ ☆

1 Doris Lessing
2 Edna O'Brien
3 Stephen King
4 *The Land That Time Forgot*
5 *Anna Of The Five Towns*

DETECTIVES AND THEIR CREATORS

1	Inspector Maigret	Georges Simenon
2	Miss Marple	Agatha Christie
3	Nero Wolfe	Rex Stout
4	Philip Marlowe	Raymond Chandler
5	Sherlock Holmes	Sir Arthur Conan Doyle
6	Father Brown	G. K. Chesterton
7	Charlie Chan	Earl Derr Biggers
8	Ellery Queen	Manfred B. Lee and Frederick Dannay
9	Lord Peter Wimsey	Dorothy L. Sayers
10	Continental Op	Dashiell Hammett

CHARACTERS FROM CLASSIC NOVELS

1	*The Prisoner Of Zenda*	Anthony Hope
2	*Wuthering Heights*	Emily Brontë
3	*Pride And Prejudice*	Jane Austen
4	*War And Peace*	Leo Tolstoy
5	*Jude The Obscure*	Thomas Hardy
6	*The Wind In The Willows*	Kenneth Grahame
7	*Sons And Lovers*	D. H. Lawrence
8	*Nicholas Nickleby*	Charles Dickens
9	*Barchester Towers*	Anthony Trollope
10	*Blott On The Landscape*	Tom Sharpe

BESTSELLERS

1	*Master Of The Game*	by Sidney Sheldon
2	*The Thornbirds*	by Colleen McCullough
3	*Penmarric*	by Susan Howatch
4	*A Woman Of Substance*	by Barbara Taylor Bradford
5	*Lace*	by Shirley Conran
6	*Roots*	by Alex Haley
7	*Valley Of The Dolls*	by Jacqueline Susann
8	*Mistral's Daughter*	by Judith Krantz
9	*79 Park Avenue*	by Harold Robbins
10	*The Winds Of War*	by Herman Wouk

THE LIVES OF ACTORS

1	William Holden	A biography by Bob Thomas
2	Shelley Winters	An autobiography
3	Peter Sellers	A biography by Michael Sellers
4	Pat Phoenix	An autobiography
5	James Mason	An autobiography
6	Petula Clark	A biography by Andrea Kon
7	Vincent Price	An autobiography
8	Bette Davis	A biography by Whitney Stine
9	Claire Bloom	An autobiography
10	Betty Grable	A biography by Doug Warren
11	Michael Caine	A biography by William Hall
12	Carroll Baker	An autobiography
13	Elizabeth Taylor	A biography by Kitty Kelley
14	Shirley Maclaine	An autobiography
15	Dirk Bogarde	The third volume of his autobiography

WHICH NOVEL?

1	*Zoo Gang*	Paul Gallico
2	*Kings Royal*	John Quigley
3	*Sorrell And Son*	Warwick Deeping
4	*Poldark*	Winston Graham
5	*The Mallens*	Catherine Cookson
6	*Testament Of Youth*	Vera Brittain
7	*Tinker, Tailor, Soldier, Spy*	John Le Carré
8	*Man At The Top*	John Braine

9	*The Saint*	Leslie Charteris
10	*The Invisible Man*	H. G. Wells
11	*Rumpole Of The Bailey*	John Mortimer
12	*Brideshead Revisited*	Evelyn Waugh
13	*Thomas The Tank Engine*	Rev. W. Awdry
14	*The Barchester Chronicles*	Anthony Trollope
15	*Roots*	Alex Haley
16	*South Riding*	Winifred Holtby
17	*Dr Kildare*	Max Brand
18	*A Voyage Round My Father*	John Mortimer
19	*The Country Diary Of An Edwardian Lady*	Edith Holden
20	*Lace*	Shirley Conran

MEMORIES ARE MADE OF THIS
1 b Darling
2 c Roald Dahl
3 d Alice (in *Alice In Wonderland*)
4 a Little Lord Fauntleroy
5 a Greyfriars
6 d *The Water Babies*
7 b Flashman
8 c Jim Hawkins
9 a Eeyore
10 c *Heidi*

THE BOOK AND THE FILM
1 James Herriot was the author. Anthony Hopkins, Simon Ward and Lisa Harrow were actors in *All Creatures Great And Small*.
2 Richard Llewellyn wrote this novel concerning childhood memories in a Welsh mining village. Walter Pidgeon, Maureen O'Hara, Roddy McDowall and Donald Crisp starred in this 1941 film.
3 John Le Carré was the author of the thriller *The Spy Who Came In From The Cold*. Leading roles in the film were played by Richard Burton, Claire Bloom and Oskar Werner.
4 L. P. Hartley wrote the twenties novel *The Hireling*. Sarah Miles, Robert Shaw and Peter Egan starred in the British film version.